Daniel J. Cherico

THEIR MOTHERS' SONS

THEIR MOTHERS' SONS

The Psychiatrist Examines
an American Problem

EDWARD A. STRECKER
A.M., M.D., Sc.D., Litt.D., LL.D.

Daniel J. Cherico

J. B. LIPPINCOTT COMPANY
PHILADELPHIA & NEW YORK

COPYRIGHT, 1946, 1951, BY
EDWARD A. STRECKER

PRINTED IN THE
UNITED STATES OF AMERICA

THIRD IMPRESSION

Library of Congress catalog card number 51-4371

FOREWORD

On April 27, 1945, Dr. Edward A. Strecker delivered a lecture before several hundred medical students and physicians at the Bellevue Hospital in New York City. The lecture, now popularly and controversially known as "the Mom lecture," was the first in a memorial lectureship established at the bequest of Dr. Menas S. Gregory, an old friend of Dr. Strecker's and up until the time of his death in 1941 a professor of psychiatry at New York University and head of the psychiatric division of Bellevue Hospital.

Dr. Strecker called his lecture, "Psychiatry Speaks to Democracy." His title understated his subject. He could have called it "Psychiatry Speaks to the Neurotic Moms of Psychoneurotics," for the darts of his comments were directed first at the apron-stringing "moms" of our nation and indirectly at their effect upon our democracy. In his lecture, Dr. Strecker pulled no verbal punches in indicting the doting "mom" for her sins of commission and omission against her children and therefore against the nation.

Dr. Strecker's background gives him the right to speak. As a well-known practicing psychiatrist, as Chairman of the Psychiatry Department at the University of Pennsylvania, and as consultant to the Surgeons General of the Army and Navy and as adviser to the Secretary of War, which work brought him in direct contact with the problems of screening men at induction centers and in the service, he has seen the case histories of many thousands of "psychoneurotics." To him the cold hard facts that 1,825,000 men were rejected for military service because of psychiatric disorders, that almost another 600,000 had been discharged from the Army alone for neuropsychiatric reasons or their equivalent, and that fully 500,000 more attempted to evade the draft were alarming statistics.

What had caused this large number of "psychoneurotics" among our young men of military age? The cold facts of the draft induction centers and service discharges are there for everyone to see, and although they are military figures they provide a definite cross-section sampling of our population. The military service screening processes gave an excellent opportunity to set up a definite measuring stick by which to evaluate the average maturity and emotional stability of our youth—their ability to face life, live with others, think for themselves, and stand on their own two feet. The figures are not promising—almost 3,000,000 men either rejected or otherwise lost to the service for neuropsychiatric reasons out of 15,000,000, just a bit under 20 per cent!

The story was not new to Dr. Strecker. For many years in the practice of psychiatry in public hospitals and privately, he had seen the handwriting of moms upon the walls of our family, community, and national houses. However, it was his observations in World War II, in the course of his psychiatric duties for the Army, Navy, and

Air Forces, both in this country and in overseas theatres, that crystallized his opinions into a warning which he felt should be given to the nation. This book is the case he presents and his warning.

EUGENE MEYER

Chairman of the National Committee on Mental Hygiene

Washington, D. C.

CONTENTS

THEIR MOTHERS' SONS

CHAPTER I

CONTRAST AND CONFLICT

First of all, I would like to define my use of the word "mom." I am not being derisive of the use of the name "Mom." Personally, I happen to prefer "Mother," but I am more than willing to subscribe to and honor the name "Mom" whenever it designates a loving but wise and mature maternal parent.

"Mom" as I have used it, and will use it throughout this book, is merely a convenient verbal hook upon which to hang an indictment of the woman who has failed in the elementary mother function of weaning her offspring emotionally as well as physically. I might have called this kind of spurious mother far less pleasant names than Mom. In treating psychoneurotics I have heard patients damn their moms in no uncertain terms and in language that would not look well in print.

The term "mom" as I propose to use it in this book is not my own invention. It has been used in the derogatory sense by numerous writers, most recently and sensationally by Philip Wylie in his *Generation of Vipers*. But Mr. Wylie's mom is described in too vindictive terms to satisfy a trained psychiatrist.

During three years of work as consultant to the Secretary of War and to the Surgeons General of the Army, Army Air Forces, and Navy, I have seen the results of both "moms" and "mothers." In my tours of casualty hospitals, both overseas and in this country, two sharply contrasting pictures were deeply etched upon my mind.

One picture I saw in many seriously wounded youngsters, particularly amputees; in combat fatigue victims who often after a few days' rest, some good food, and a little encouragement were back in the line fighting as well as ever; in the many thousands of young Americans in England eagerly and impatiently preparing for D-Day.

The other picture, a sad contrast, I saw in the NP (neuropsychiatric) wards of Army and Navy hospitals in this country—tens of thousands of the vague manifestations of the so-called psychoneuroses—backaches by the score, for which meticulous and exhaustive medical examinations failed to uncover any bodily reason; headaches, infinite in variety, but inexplainable on the basis of physical disturbances; hundreds of cases of just plain "tiredness" or "don't-feel-right"; and dozens of other mysterious complaints. No amount of reassurance, encouragement, or treatment would bring response from these patients. It was like trying to push back a wall of water. There was nothing solid to grasp.

War is a great leveler. It strips the soft, protective swathings of civilian life from millions of young men and exposes them to a threat to survival. It brings out their strengths and reveals their weaknesses both physical and mental. Frequently, the scales of war are heavily weighted against the chances of physical and emotional survival—sometimes even against the wish to survive. Often the last ounce of body strength and more than that—everything a man was, is, and hopes to be—must be thrown into the balance before it tips in his favor.

During the closing months of the war, I paid periodic visits to the first hospital station to which wounded soldiers were brought from the European theater. Between each two beds in the wards there was an arrangement by which a phone could be plugged in and the patients could call their homes. The first time I overheard snatches of these conversations, tears came to my eyes. I hope I never lose the feeling of reverence I experienced whenever I heard these youngsters talking to their mothers and their families, making light of the loss of an arm or a leg.

To this picture, too, there belong many psychiatric battle casualties like true combat fatigue. Here in violent nightmares, the horror of war experiences is lived again, the victim *seeing,* not remembering but *seeing,* his closest friend suddenly slump into death at his side, his friends clinging to a life raft swept by enemy fire, the agony of being trapped in the boiler compartment of a torpedoed and sinking ship. Small wonder that even months after the actual experience, these men when awakened from nightmares grasp at any outstretched hand, clinging to it like terrorized children.

No doubt you have seen someone trembling with fear.

Raise the trembling to the nth degree and you have the startle reflex of combat fatigue—a severe and generalized tremor, started by any sudden, casual sound like the slam of a door or the setting of a dish heavily on the table. Such innocent sounds flood the unconscious mind, the mind that does not remember yet never forgets, with reverberations of combat sounds that spelled disaster, suffering, and death.

All of us have seen men and women who are uneasy and troubled by self-blame. Such ordinary self-reproof is a pale thing compared to the black shadows of guilt which envelop many combat fatigue patients. Time and time again I've heard such things as—"I should have swum out and helped Bill." "Yes, Doctor, I know I was ordered to bail out, but all the same maybe if I hadn't I might have stopped Jack's bleeding and he'd be alive today." "If I hadn't tripped over those roots and made a noise those lousy Japs wouldn't have got George." And so the usual pattern goes—"perhaps," "maybe," "if," —silently accusing fingers of guilt.

A few months after the close of the war, several combat fatigue patients from an Army Air Forces Hospital attended a Rotarian luncheon in a western city. The toastmaster announced that a local boy, Jim Robinson, missing for a long time and given up as killed, had turned up as a prisoner of war, would be home in a few days, and would attend the next week's luncheon. At this point, one of the combat fatigue patients broke in excitedly requesting further identification of Jim Robinson. When it was given, he exclaimed, "Thank God. I thought he was dead and that it was my fault. You see I was briefed for a mission over Berlin. I didn't go because I was sick and Robinson went in my place. He didn't come back. Then I began to think that maybe I wasn't so sick. Maybe I could have gone on that mission. I felt maybe if I'd done my duty Robinson would not have lost his life. Thank God he's alive. I'm cured now."

All in all, true combat fatigue comprises a group of upstanding young men who could not be broken until great hardships, deprivations, exhaustion, and soul-searing emotional experiences were loaded upon them. They were as honorably wounded as though they had been struck down by enemy fire.

A twenty-two-year-old seaman was trapped with twenty other men below deck on a light aircraft carrier in the Tarawa assault. He kept on swimming, holding up one of his companions while the compartment filled with water. Overcome by fright and exhaustion, one by one the other men gave up and were drowned. After many hours, a rescue party reached the survivor through an overhead hatch. He was still holding up his friend.

When he reached topside he was fearful and cried. He would not go below deck. When he was evacuated to a mainland hospital he had periodic recurrences of anxiety panics, precipitated by loud noises. At first, he had frequent nightmares in which he relived his experience. With appropriate treatment, however, he was well in twelve weeks.

This is the stuff of which the sons of mothers are made.

The mothers of men who fought valiantly and returned unharmed and the mothers of men who were seriously wounded—who had lost a leg or an arm and could joke about it, and those who were honorably "wounded" by severe combat and operational fatigue—need no decorations or citations to memorialize the service of their sons. They brought into the world sturdy flesh, blood, and sinew and activated it with the spirit of indomitable morale. That is enough. They are mothers of mature men—men who can and who are willing to meet life whether it be a civilian or a military life.

Not so with most of the 500,000 men who tried to evade service to their country—draft dodgers who resorted to any device, however shameful, even to the wearing of female clothing. Not so with the majority of the 1,825,000 men who were rejected at induction for various neuropsychiatric causes. Not so with a large proportion of the 600,000 more that had to be discharged from the service for similar reasons. Most of these men could not face the prospects of an exacting and unsure military life.

What was the difference between those men who failed on the battlefield and those who failed long before they reached it? Which of these classes and which men in these classes were sick?

They were *all* sick. Those psychiatric battle casualties, who served splendidly and broke only after an overload of physical strain and emotional stress beyond the limits of average endurance was placed upon them, were sick. Those men, too, were sick who made a feeble attempt at service but soon after induction, sometimes only a few days, retreated under the cloak of neurotic symptoms. Likewise were those men sick who failed to clear the induction hurdle because they were weighted by psycho-neurotic impediments, often directly traceable to serious deficits in motivation, or because their previous behavior records were bad enough to make them unacceptable. Finally, even the least of them were sick, too, those who did not make even the gesture of service and attempted to dodge the draft in one way or another.

The solution of any human emotional conflict, the compromise which is arrived at, depends not only, or even chiefly, on the nature and gravity of the problem but on the strength of the contending forces engaged in the psychic battle. We never can bring more into the battle than we have. We are what we are; we are as strong as our strength. Not only were all these men sick; the symptoms of the sickness represented a serious inner emotional conflict that was common to all—self-preservation versus soldierly ideals.

Such a conflict is a silent, grim, unconscious struggle. On one side are the numerous behavior demands of one of our most ancient endowments—self-preservation. So insistent and so dominant is it that it operates automatically not only in attempting to remove us from danger but even in striving to protect us from life's small discomforts.

On the other side, strongly opposing this and engaging in psychological combat with it, is a mixture of behavior patterns, which in this instance can be labeled "soldierly ideals." Even at rumors of war there comes into the minds of every man who might be called into military service thoughts of the requirements that go with being a soldier. Soldierly ideals consist of instilled complex behavior patterns—realistic considerations such as the fear of being shot for cowardice in battle; practical considerations, like the desire to finish "this dirty job and get home as soon as possible"; more idealistic drives, "this is my duty and I am going to do it well." Various higher levels may be attained and sometimes summits are reached, such as the determination to fight and, if need be, die for the preservation of democracy.

The same struggle—self-preservation against threats to life or even to the slightest encroachment upon our physical comfort and ease—exists in our everyday civilian existence. It is not peculiar to military life. No matter how deeply buried in thought we may be, the instinct for self-preservation is always vigilant. When an automobile horn sounds, we automatically jump to one side without thinking. If we are taking a badly needed nap, we resent the ring of the telephone. Within us, whether in peace or in war, the lance of self-preservation is always crossed against the lance of any outward influence that might injure us or disturb our normal course.

The pattern of the underlying emotional conflict was the same in those men who fought bravely and succumbed to neuropsychiatric disabilities and in those whose nervous systems broke though they did not serve. The general markings of the pattern are identical.

However, while the conflict is the same in both groups, the manner in which it is fought is vastly different. In those who "took it," the available *motivation* and *determination* which was exerted—in other words, the amount of effort that was expended—in attempting to control the behavior dictated by the demands of self-preservation, was at a high level. In the others, those who could not take it, the struggle was weak and ineffectual, and the control approached the vanishing point. Self-preservation in these men ran amuck.

Why did the desire for self-preservation defeat one group of men, to their discredit, and not the other? The answer in ninety percent of the cases can be given in one word, IMMATURITY. The majority of the men who failed, like the majority of the men who fail for the same reasons in ordinary life, were IMMATURE.

For the moment let us look at the meaning of this word immaturity. Or, better yet, let us look at the positive side of the picture—maturity.

What constitutes maturity? In conversation most of us mean a man is mature when he is grown up. Webster defines it simply as the *state or quality of being mature; ripeness, full development,* but it is much more than that. It is a complex mixture of personality qualities. It is the ability to see a job through, no matter what. It is the inherent desire always to give more than is asked for or required in any given situation. It is the quality of dependability that makes other people say, "There's a reliable person." It is independence of thought and action. Maturity represents the capacity to cooperate, to work with others, to work in an organization, and to work under authority. The mature person is pliable and can alter his own desires according to time, persons, and circumstances. He is tolerant, he is patient, he is adaptable —he is human. Maturity is the mark of good morale in the individual.

CHAPTER II

THE MOTHER'S DILEMMA

Maturity is not an inborn trait; it is not hereditary. It is the result of early background, environment, training, and unselfish parental love.

Conversely, immaturity is caused by the lack of a good intelligent foundation in this business of living. It is not difficult to find basic reasons for immaturity. Often it is merely necessary to retrace the life of an immature person. Given the opportunity of having known when he was eight to twelve years old, any one of the men who failed in his opportunity to serve in the armed forces because of neuropsychiatric tendencies, and, particularly, of having known his mother, a competent psychiatrist could have forecast with reasonable accuracy the boy's future immaturity. In the vast majority of case histories, a "mom" is at fault.

Every woman who bears children is confronted by a dilemma from which there is no escape. The dilemma is as old as the human race, yet its implications and its dangers are peculiarly a part of our closely knit modern civilization and its intricate social cultures. Upon the successful solution of the dilemma depends not only the welfare of a mother's children but, in a large part, the basic survival of the nation of which her children are to be the future citizens and statesmen. The solution is not easy and the stakes are high. No nation is in greater danger of failing to solve the mother-child dilemma than our own nation. No nation would have to pay as great a penalty as the United States for not solving it.

The future social behavior of a child has its beginning and is patterned in the conflicting sensations and emotions that arise from the early relationship between the mother and child. For the child, the mother is not only the great Dispenser of pleasure and love and the great Protectress, but also the source of pain, the ruthless Thwarter and Frustrater. So the dilemma of the mother is likewise the dilemma of the child. It is a delicately balanced conflict of clinging and rejecting and, depending on which way the balance is tipped, the child either learns to meet successfully the larger give-and-take aspects of mature living or he doesn't. If the give-and-take capacity is not developed, the child will fail to adjust himself to his own life and to society. As a result, the child never grows up. He remains emotionally immature.

Weaning is as much a part of motherhood as is nursing. Taking away from a child is as important as giving to it. Rejecting and emancipating a child are as significant as clinging to it. Furthermore, these seemingly contradictory phases of motherhood belong to each other both in nature and in sequence.

A play would be incomplete and meaningless if it stopped at the end of the first act, or if the last act were given without the first. Likewise with the mother-child relationship. The phase of taking away from or the rejection of the child by the mother would not only be ineffective but also senseless cruelty unless it had been preceded by the clinging and protective phase. On the other hand, the child who has known nothing but protection and has only learned to take and not to give has been sadly defrauded by his mother—so badly cheated that it would have been better if he had never been born.

Within the limits of the sensory, emotional, and social motherhood-relationship, there is in miniature each child's future. The world we live in drives a hard bargain in the business of giving and taking. It never gives of the largeness of its satisfactions, unless it receives an equally valuable deposit in the general social account. The adult who as a child was never taught to share and give and concede or to think and act independently can almost never learn to do so later in life. There is a tragic finality about childhood. Unfortunately, the vast majority of men and women are made or broken before the first ten years of their lives have been completed.

What happens to the child whose mother not only has failed to sever the emotional apron strings but often has not even loosened them? His natural gregarious instincts lead him to seek social relations with his fellow man. But, because he has only learned to take, he sooner or later is rebuffed. He becomes a bystander in the game of life—a sad, disillusioned and envious spectator. He cannot be a lone wolf, living apart from his fellow man. Few men succeed in doing that and he least of all. Psychologically, it would mean his eventual emotional annihilation.

A few months ago, a young man in his middle twenties came to the office of one of my associates. He had had no appointment; he had just "come in on the chance that he could see someone who could help him." At first his chief complaint was "spells"—spells that he had tried to cure with rigid daily exercise and strict dietary programs.

He is an intelligent young man, a college graduate and the holder of a graduate degree from one of our well-known universities, yet on his first visit he felt sure he had some sort of strange digestive disorder; he spoke continually of "constipation and intestinal poisons."

As he described his "spells" he made various mentions of his mother and her opinions regarding his "trouble." The more he talked the more he brought the word "mother" into his conversation. Then, bit by bit, the real story came to the surface.

Ever since his childhood his mother, or more properly his mom, has dominated him. After college, when he left home to take a well-paying job in another city, she carried on her domination by long-distance telephone. She repeatedly accused him of shirking his responsibility as a son in spite of the fact that he was contributing more toward her support than either of his two brothers. As a result he finally gave up his job to take another that paid less and promised less of a future so that he could live at home. Now she continually reminds him, "Harry, you are head of the house now. If you go away again you will be throwing up your responsibility."

In spite of his twenty-six years, he has never had a date with a girl—he "knows" that his mom would not approve. Even mild flirtations in the office in which he works upset him. At the time he enjoys them, but when he gets to thinking about them he wonders "what mom would say?"

The psychiatrist treating him suggested that he assert himself and move away from his mother, reminding him that he could still see that she lived comfortably and free from want. She was healthy; it was not a case of a sick woman requiring care. He agreed and berated his mother for her dominance, but when he arrived for his next appointment he admitted that he had been unable to make the break. His mother had gone into one of her emotional tirades and had even threatened to take the matter to court.

This mom's boy realizes that his life is being ruined, yet, at the moment, he is unable to do anything about it. He lacks the decision of a mature person. He wants freedom, he wants the normal companionship of girls, he wants a normal adult man's life, yet he is completely submerged and confused. With careful guidance he will mature and emerge. He has not had one of his "spells" since his second visit. But it is a fight that will take a good deal of emotional strength. Unfortunately, he is no isolated case—there are thousands like him.

I know of another young man who was completely mom-dominated up until the time he entered the service. As a matter of fact, I have always strongly suspected that he enlisted long before his draft call to escape his mom. During his time in the army, his mom accepted his absence more or less "unselfishly" as a matter of course. He is back home now—a grown man, honorably discharged after three years of fighting in the South Pacific —yet mom is very much upset because he wants to go out nights rather than stay at home with her. She complains, "He's changed. He goes out at night and doesn't get home until late."

Many men, even though they recognize parental dominance, unfortunately never free themselves. I know of one case in which a man up to the day of his death, some fifteen years after the death of his mom, had never succeeded in doing the things he really wanted to do. Mom died when he was 52 and up until that time he had never been to the theater, to church, on a vacation, or to a social gathering without her. Even after her death, in spite of the fact that he wanted a normal life, he could not bring himself to the point of feeling completely free to live as he wished. His mom's dominance, like many another's, lived much longer than she did.

And it is not always the son who suffers. I have known many a young woman who has realized that she was being dominated by her mom and upon the mom's death first experienced a feeling of freedom and release, but ultimately has lived strictly according to her mom's selfish code. Always the subconscious thought was, "What would mom think if I did that?"

The responsibilities of motherhood are great.

CHAPTER III

MOM AND HER SILVER CORD

What constitutes a mom? How does she differ from a mother? Fundamentally, a mom is not a mother. Mom is a maternal parent who fails to prepare her offspring emotionally for living a productive adult life on an adult social plane. A mom does not untie the emotional apron string—the Silver Cord—which binds her children to her.

Moms are just about as old as parenthood. For years in my practice I have seen moms and the sad result of moms. My work in the Army and the Navy, because it gave me the chance to study over a short period thousands of psychoneurotics, served to add to my case histories of moms.

I look at mom without rancor or resentment and not without understanding. Mom is not of her own making. Various forces work together to produce her kind. The basic mosaic of her behavior in most cases was put together in her own childhood without her knowledge and without her consent. Furthermore, momism is the product of a social system veering toward a matriarchy in which each individual mom plays only a small part.

Outwardly, a mom is not distinctively marked. She may be fat or thin; tall or small; blond, brunette, or a redhead, or she may wear a halo of motherly silvered hair. She may be beautiful or uncomely, dress dashingly or dowdily. She may be a college graduate or she may not. She may be quite ignorant of Emily Post's dicta, or she may be gracious and charming.

However, she does have one thing in common—the emotional satisfaction, almost repletion, she derives from keeping her children paddling about in a kind of psychological amniotic fluid rather than letting them swim away with the bold and decisive strokes of maturity from the emotional maternal womb.

There is nothing stronger in this world than the child-mother cohesion. A mother song in a bar or from the stage of the cheapest burlesque will bring lumps in the throats and tears to the eyes of the roughest and toughest men. For all of us there is a natural pull back to mother.

While I was in London during the middle stages of the war, I had the chance to talk informally with a group of young but hardened combat pilots on a few days' leave after months of flying over Germany and the continent. Life to them was a matter of expert maneuvering and a quick hand on the trigger button of the control stick. They were no milksops, but men who faced death every time they took to the air. Their lives depended on their guts, their daring, and their flying ability. As inevitably happens in soldier bull sessions, the conversation finally turned to sex. Several of them admitted that they had tried to satisfy the sex urge during their leave, but had not succeeded. Suddenly, they had discovered that what they wanted after all was not sexual intercourse but merely to be held, caressed, and petted by a woman —just as a mother would fondle her baby. It was natural enough. Young children who have narrowly escaped some danger instinctively rush back to their mother's arms to be comforted and quieted. Interestingly, in the South Pacific, Bing Crosby received more requests to sing Brahms' "Lullaby" than any other song.

A mom will take advantage of this natural mother urge to hold her child or children to her. The real mother fights the urge and lovingly does everything in her power to make her children stand on their own feet. She prepares them for an adult life. The mothers of men and women capable of facing life maturely are not apt to be the traditional mom type. More likely mom is sweet, doting, "self-sacrificing." But the obverse of this cast, the capable stern, self-contained domineering mom is not uncommon.

Silver cords come in varying lengths. Sometimes they are short, mere tether ropes, with both ends always in plain view. Not long ago I heard two moms boasting that their sixteen- and seventeen-year-old children had never slept a single night away from their homes. "When bedtime comes, kiddies want to be tucked in," they concluded with satisfaction.

More often, however, silver cords are much longer and much more difficult to trace. Seemingly they allow a wide range of freedom, but it is surprising how quickly they can be drawn taut and gathered in should the children roam too near strange pastures.

The best blueprint comparisons between mothers and moms that I have ever seen were the letters received by men in the service from their mothers and moms. No professional writers have ever plucked the emotional heartstrings more expertly than the moms who wrote some of the letters I have read.

A woman, prominent in official Washington, told me of a typical case. A woman she knew had a son in an Army camp. Shortly after his induction, the mother wrote to the boy, begging him to return home at once, since she was having one of her "sick spells." The sick spells were merely hysterical tantrums, and furthermore this mom was in affluent circumstances and expert medical help was available. The boy replied that he would very much like to come home to see her but that at the moment no furloughs were being granted and that he would be A.W.O.L. if he left camp, a court-martial offense. The mom answered with a letter that was a masterpiece of pathos. Through it ran an ominous undercurrent of what might happen to her if her "only boy" didn't come to see her. It even implied that he might not see his mother alive again. The boy showed the letter to his officer, but since the deception was obvious no furlough was granted. The boy went A.W.O.L. and was court-martialed, receiving rather mild punishment. Thereupon, his mom wrote to her friend, the woman in Washington. It was a vituperative letter that reviled her friend's husband and everyone in office from the President down. Unless the officer who had ordered her son's court-martial was punished, something very serious would happen. Perhaps there would be a Congressional investigation. No, this woman was not insane. She was merely a mom at her worst.

One of my students, a naval officer who had served in the Pacific through the toughest campaigns, recently told me of a number of instances in which Marines awaiting combat orders had received letters from moms, setting forth dramatically their maternal anguish and, in one instance, begging a son to feign illness in order to avoid the dangers of combat. In their anxiety and distress in mind, the men brought the letters to their medical officer. One Marine was in such a state of turmoil and tension that the doctor sent him to the hospital on the eve of a battle, since, emotionally upset and indecisive as he was, he would scarcely have had a fair chance to come through with his life and probably would have endangered the lives of others.

The typical mom letter to her son invariably whines and complains, gives a gloomy picture of the home situation, and is heavily perfumed with sickly sentimentality masquerading as love. In my tours through the various camps and bases during the war, I saw hundreds of lonely youngsters trying desperately to make the grade, attempting to acclimate themselves psychologically to military life, who were completely broken by a typical mom letter which filled their minds with worries about home and particularly about mom. The final result in a large percentage of the cases studied was a discharge for "psychoneurosis."

I have seen similar things happen at boarding schools and summer camps—young boys trying hard to cast off the silver cords only to be sent home finally for failure or homesickness induced by letters from mom or visits from mom. A camp counsellor (they call them group leaders at some camps) recently told me, "If the doting mothers would only forget to write, we might be able to make men of their kids. They spend money to send them here; then they ruin it all by keeping close home contacts." He could have said "silver cords," and been closer to the cause.

There is nothing finer, on the other hand, than a letter from a real mother to her young son who is in the service or otherwise away from home. It does not preach. It praises and encourages, soothes homesickness, and bolsters morale. Above all, it is cheerful and chatty and seldom mentions minor illnesses or home problems.

I wish more women could have written such letters. I am sure if they had, the figure of 600,000 discharges for "neuropsychiatric reasons" would have been considerably less.

CHAPTER IV

NEAR MOTHERS AND NEAR MOMS

It would be an error to assume that there is a clear-cut line of cleavage between mothers and moms, between motherhood and momism. If being a mother is understood to be a function consisting solely of rigorously preparing a child for mature emotional and social existence, then fortunately there are no such mothers. Such a Spartan-like figure would be a grotesque anomaly and a caricature of true motherhood. No normal woman can produce a child, give it life and love, and nurture and protect it when it is a helpless infant without creating a close bond that never can be completely broken. This is as it should be.

Theoretically, a mom is a woman whose maternal behavior is motivated by the seeking of emotional recompense for the buffets which life has dealt her own ego. In her relationship with her children, every deed and almost every breath are designed unconsciously but exclusively to absorb her children emotionally and to bind them to her securely. In order to achieve this purpose she must stamp a pattern of immature behavior in her children. Such a pattern is entirely inconsistent with even a minimum degree of adequacy and satisfaction and completely excludes the possibility of living life in an adult manner. With such a rigid criteria, probably there are not many bona fide moms, although I have known a few women who have almost succeeded in reaching the summits of momism.

Actually, in every mother, no matter how mature she may be, there are traces of mom. There should be. Likewise, in moms there are odds and ends and fragments of motherhood although sometimes they are ultramicroscopic. However, there is a deal of difference in the amounts of these ingredients in mothers and moms, and the driving forces which activate motherly and momish behaviors are as far apart as the poles.

The mature mother uses the emotional ingredients sparingly and wisely. Her major purpose is to produce a proper balance of give-and-take in her children, so that they may attain full-statured personal and social maturity and lead reasonably constructive and happy lives. The immature and insatiable mom, on the other hand, uses the ingredients lavishly and unwisely, chiefly to bind her children with emotional coils. Being immature herself, she breeds immaturity in her children and, by and large, they are doomed to lives of personal and social insufficiency and unhappiness.

In her dealings with her children, the real mother mixes logic with her love and at every step attempts to lead her children into thinking for themselves. In matters requiring judgment in selection, whether it be clothes or opinions, the mother knows her children need guidance but in decreasing amounts and with the objective of increasing self-decision. After all, Mary who is fifteen can hardly have that very décolleté evening gown for her first party frock no matter how much she wants it. Neither can Ann who is only in her 'teens be indulged in the filmy, black-lace underthings that her heart desires.

Likewise, the real mother knows that the home should be an informal forum where the children's opinions will be listened to and discussed pro and con. Discussions so conducted that the child realizes that his parents are interested in his ideas often trims down wild and adolescent thinking, and leaves the nucleus of a sound thought. Surprisingly often, a parental challenge to read this or that article or book is accepted.

A mother knows that a home in which children live should be comfortable and pleasant and supply their reasonable needs—a place where they like to bring other children and which other children enjoy visiting. There need not be many restrictions, but there must be a few regulations. To have the right kind of a home, it is not necessary to do as some moms do, letting the door mat symbolize a wishing rug, capable of granting every whim as soon as the door is opened.

Probably it rarely enters the mind of a mother—yet if she were questioned about it, no doubt she would reply honestly—that if there were the need for help and support, because of sickness or old age, she would feel entitled to it from her children. Unlike mom, however, she would not permit her children to immolate themselves upon her altar of need, but would insist on disarranging the lives of her children as little as possible.

A sensible mother would at once detect the artificial nonsense of the pollyanna mom with her unbroken circle of familial joy and harmony. She knows that children are adults in the making and, if adults never disagreed, contended, argued, and even occasionally quarreled, then they would eventually be at each other's throats to escape the sheer monotony and boredom of complete and unending concord.

Without being either pugnacious or devious, the mother knows how to interpose quiet, diplomatic intervention against unfair or oversevere criticisms of a child by the father or the other children. She does this difficult job simply and with due regard for the merits of the situation and for the personal rights of each member of the family. Her middle-of-the-road policy avoids the risk either of dangerously inflating the child's ego or of plunging him into the depths of inferiority.

The mother permits her children considerable latitude of thought and behavior, but she realizes that the only time the "musts" and "must nots" of the world of adults can be learned is during childhood. It is obvious that there must be "musts" and "must nots." Not only must children brush their teeth, keep dental appointments, bathe, and do many unpleasant things, but also there are many alluring things they must *not* do.

Some moms reveal the immature markings of their motherhood by the constant exercise of unqualified and unexplained authority. More ensnare their children by letting them do practically anything they wish. The mother's "musts" and "must nots" are usually qualified and self-explanatory. The objective of mothers is to make an increasing reservoir of self-criticism and inhibition available against the temptation to impulsive behavior.

Irrespective of their physical endowments or the amount of intellectual information they have had opportunity to acquire, even though it is minimal, mothers could never be inconsequential addlepates or pseudo-intellectuals. Not that the mother sees any virtue for herself or her children in being drab or dowdily dressed. Not unlikely, she subscribes to the code of the "hair-do," cosmetics, and other beauty aids which modern life have made almost mandatory. The mother, too, does not believe that the functions of motherhood include being a dumbbell. On the contrary, generally she informs herself as fully as circumstances permit and she is likely to be able to present her opinions in an interesting way. While she may give little or no conscious thought to it, the mother in considerable degree is activated by the fact that constantly she is mirroring a reflection for her children, a detailed portrait revealing every asset, but also every imperfection, and covering a wide surface from physical appearance and grooming to mental agility. Unlike the reflection mirrored by the mom, too often a trap which confines the child's future and circumvents his emotional choices in life, the mother portrait is undeliberate and natural. As the child grows older, the portrait merges into rapidly increasing personal contacts and is progressively modified. There remains a nucleus or essence which serves as a useful starting point and lessens the child's danger of making immature and crippling emotional alliances in adult life. The reflection of the mom binds children; the likeness of the mother unleashes them and beckons them on to emotional and social emancipation.

Guarding the health of their children is difficult for mothers. Many moms solve it easily by intoning an endless litany of warnings about everything from overshoes to vitamins. The mother either knows or senses the danger of ingraining too deeply a pattern of oversolicitude about health and physical processes. Neurasthenia is an oddly shaped piece which will not fit into the jigsaw puzzle of life. The mother is seriously but sensibly concerned about the health of her children. She tries to inculcate normal common-sense caution without impressing fears of sickness, accident, and death. Usually she succeeds in establishing a happy compromise. In obtaining such a compromise the mother does not hesitate occasionally to take minor chances by not always being too insistent about overshoes or nosedrops.

The mom regards the fence with which children surround their private thinking as a lien upon her emotional domain and tries to demolish it; the mother respects the privacy it incloses. Instinctively the latter knows that such mental territory should be sacred against trespass. No matter how vaporish, planless, and wildly romantic youthful thinking may be, still it is important in shaping emotional and social individualism and in promoting maturity. Should the private thinking become excessive and the child show increasing isolation from other children and the environment, the mother usually can find quiet, tactful ways of being let in on the secret.

The mother gives her children a reasonably sound and healthy sex perspective, without finding it necessary either to compose a paean to Eros or a hymn of sexual hate. Her own mistakes and disappointments are not permitted to distort the perspective. She does not visit her failures in sexual life upon her children. On the other hand, sex is not presented as unalloyed bliss exempt from responsibility or penalties for too much taking and not enough giving. The mother produces healthy attitudes more by her general reaction when the subject comes up casually; less and usually very little by studied and planned verbal instruction. She avoids pollyannish aphorisms and soothing bromides. She does not paint a precisely detailed picture, knowing that one person's sexual life cannot be modeled upon that of another and that the removal of spontaneity is destructive. Sex is not nakedly exposed. Enough of its inner veilings are left intact, so that later in life the child will have the satisfaction and the maturing value of making his own discoveries. The mother does not hope or wish to do more for her children than to give them sufficient honest information and the nucleus of receptive and favorable attitudes toward sex. This done, she may give them Godspeed upon their sexual journeys through life with the feeling that, at least, they will have an even chance of not stumbling too often or too seriously and of achieving mature sexual happiness.

Not so with many moms. Of all moms, probably the cruelest is the one who closes the door of her children's lives against the vista of normal and wholesome sex and fastens it securely with her silver cord. Unconsciously avenging herself for the disappointments, frustrations, and thwartings of her own sex life, ruthlessly she divests sex of all its beauty and makes it seem ugly and even loathsome. She may do this directly as she imparts "the facts of life" to her daughters and sometimes even to her sons. She would have it appear that men are lustful carnivora prowling about the world seeking females to devour. "So few men are considerate in that way." "They don't care to what they subject a woman or how they break down her health as long as they have their pleasure." "A woman must be constantly on guard."

With her sons mom varies the theme: "Girls are different these days," the implication being that they are very different from the kind of a girl mom was. Too few girls are sweet and modest. Deliberately and shamelessly they use their sex charms to trap unwary young men. "Before you know it, it is too late and you have wronged the nice girl you might want to marry some day."

Fair enough, but unfortunately, the "nice girl" is drawn to such meticulous specifications that the chances of finding her are somewhat remote. Even should he find a girl resembling mom's blueprint how can he be sure? She may be one of those female werewolves mom warned him about.

Contrary to the belief of some moms, the men in the armed forces, other than her son, were not sexually un- clean. My contact with them in two wars has led me to conclude that, by and large, they were decent youngsters, basically clean minded. They did not wear their hopes, aspirations, and ideals about sex upon their sleeves and only rarely did they reveal them to their fellow soldiers. There was quite a little lusty sex talk when men were gathered together in encampments and on ships. So is there in civilian life. But the sex-frightened youngsters listening to these discussions, somewhat Chaucerian in flavor, fascinated though they were, still were likely to feel that their worst fears had been confirmed. Here was the proof of what mom had said. There was an ugly, writhing morass called sex.

So beginning with the mom, by a process of addition and subtraction—adding very considerably to the faint, vague mother stuff that is in her, subtracting liberally her extravagant interpretation of the protective function of motherhood and her gross distortion of it—we arrive at the mother. In her daily life she writes a visible text of living for her children. It is neither an exact nor a highly emotionalized text. Either would be hampering in adult life. The text is a frank one, setting forth the mother's liabilities as well as her virtues. For the children, it always remains a human document, alive and realistic. The life of the mother will never be slavishly imitated. Rather will it be used for comparative purposes. Some of it will be selected for use in adult life. Some portions will be discarded, either because they are not considered applicable or because the individual feels he can do better.

Neither mothers nor moms are immune to divorce. Mothers, however, are more apt to tolerate difficult and unsatisfactory marriages for a long time, fearing the damaging effect of divorce upon the children and the hazard to their futures. They are likely to postpone decision until they are honestly convinced that the conditions of the marital situation entail a greater risk for the children than would a legal split. Moms are less thoughtful. Often in the home they erect mother-child citadels and busy themselves strengthening the defensive outposts. Husbands find it increasingly difficult to storm the defenses and many of them take the few remaining steps necessary to separate them from a situation to which already they are more or less alien.

Obviously divorce is a hazardous business for children. Lacking the information and the intelligence to make mature judgments, at first they feel chiefly its emotional impact. Perhaps the divorce itself is less harmful than the attitude of the contending parents. Too often, ex-wives and ex-husbands do everything in their power to instill into the children distrust and even hatred of their former marital partners.

Divorce leads to treacherous terrain and sometimes even mothers stumble, yielding temporarily to the temptation of bringing a bill of indictment against the father before the tribunal of the children. For the mom, the post-divorce terrain is a happy hunting ground. Mom always packs her gun and seldom neglects an opportunity of taking a potshot at her ex-husband. Her marksmanship is not excellent and often she succeeds in inflicting mortal psychological wounds upon the innocent bystanders—her children.

The technique of employing but few words is better adapted for this purpose, provided the words are carefully selected: "I tried my best; I wonder where I failed . . ."; "I couldn't help showing my love for you children . . ."; "I had to protect my children. . . ." These are very effective statements conjuring up the vision of a roaring selfish male seeking to devour the young who have usurped his place. More potent than the words are their accompaniments—occasionally a sob or two, a few tears, a catch in the throat, the patient little smile, the fierce hugs and kisses, and perhaps a sudden "sick spell." Sometimes a sad silence after a son has spoken a roughly impatient word. Only very hesitatingly does the mom confess why so suddenly she is saddened:

"Because *he* used to speak to me that way." The odds are better than even that one of the children at least will remain permanently marriage-shy, and that several of them will retain such distorted emotional reactions about marriage that their own marital ventures will end in disastrous failures. Sometimes a bull's-eye is scored when a son decides he will never marry but will stay with mom, tenderly caring for her and making up to her for the sufferings she so bravely endured in her marital life. Certainly some moms write into the bill of divorcement an invisible clause which in effect is a chattel mortgage upon the emotional lives of their children and their future social security.

Some children have amazing resilience. They only appear to be taken in. Actually they are not and have an attitude of amused and affectionate tolerance toward mom. One youngster discussing with me the overprotective behavior of his mother and the embarrassments it caused him concluded: "It's all right; it makes mom happy." I do not mean that these children who are wise beyond their generation escape scot-free, but apparently they are not seriously handicapped.

There are moms who deserve almost to be called mothers. They accomplish varying degrees of emotional and social growth for their children, or at least they do not retard it. For some of the youngsters with "near mothers" the Army provided the much needed opportunity. Here the maturing emotional and social stature could be stretched to its fullest extent. The growth was speeded up in a favorable environment and completed in average time.

Some real mothers are sadly handicapped by conditions of life which seriously interfere with attempts to give their children the full benefits of motherhood. Not infrequently the interference comes from the husband, or perhaps from relatives living in the same house. I have known a number of such mothers, and it is not surprising that often they were deeply discouraged and alarmed by the children's behavior. However, they continued the struggle, applying whatever antidotes to immaturity they could find at hand and blocking as best they could the more obvious paths to emotional dependency. It was not an easy task, but usually these mothers wrought better than they knew.

I know intimately one such situation. A boy's conduct was the replica of his father's who was still hopelessly in the thrall of his own mother's dominance, which he had come to hate but against which he was able to exert only feeble struggles. The father was unable to extricate himself from his mother's incessant demands for daily phone calls, visits, and detailed reports of his every act in life. In fact he was hopelessly enmeshed by all those devices by which a typical mom keeps her children enslaved irrespective of their ages or conditions of life. In his own home he was comfortable, provided he was not asked to help his wife in making decisions concerning the children or other important family problems. If pressed about an urgent matter which had to be settled, he would either sulk for days or have an hysterical paroxysm in which sometimes he inflicted upon himself minor bodily injuries. Nonetheless, this man had an excellent intellectual and mathematical mind and was successful in his profession of engineering. The money he earned would have sufficed had he been willing to permit its sensible distribution. As it was, his wife was usually engaged in pulling upon both ends of the finances, striving desperately to make them meet. The husband's mom was affluent and granted lend-lease loans. Unlike the return rate of lend lease in international finance, the repayment rate to moms in the coin of emotional exchange is usurious and is exacted to the last penny.

When the son of this house reached the father-hero-worship age, he modeled himself closely upon his father. Even for a boy in his early 'teens he was hopelessly untidy in his person, in his room, and in the house. He had the same talent as his father—in that a few minutes after he entered a room its contents looked as though they had been twisted by a cyclone. In his conduct he was unpredictable and usually irresponsible. Generally, he defaulted the few important engagements and obligations of his life. His behavior in school, scholastically and otherwise, was completely unsatisfactory. His teachers liked him, but were quite discouraged and suggested vaguely that some day he might grow up.

The boy was devoted to his mother, and, of course, he visited upon her his dissatisfactions and his reaction to the penalties for things he did, or more often, for the things he did not do. The mother did a good job of sitting tight. She did not reveal much of her deep emotional concern and only occasionally lost her temper. She was always ready and willing to help with his lessons and the emergencies of his childhood life. Invariably her help was in the direction of devising self-decision techniques, hoping the boy might be stimulated to help himself. As to his behavior in the home, the mother stood firmly but kindly and understandingly on the platform that he owed some contribution to the family in terms of conduct.

Then came December 7, 1941. Just a few days past his seventeenth birthday, the boy went to an enlistment station and signified his desire of joining up. Defiantly and, I think, rather hopeful of touching off an explosion, he informed his mother. There was no explosion. Instead there was a not too satisfactory interview, in which the mother urged the advisability of staying in school a few more months, a course which would leave less scholastic ground to be covered should the boy later wish to secure a diploma. This would not interfere with his proposed enlistment. Privately the youngster talked it over with the old non-com at the enlistment station and, when the recruiting sergeant said he thought it a good idea, the boy concurred.

Then followed a period of behavior which anyone but a skilled psychiatrist who knew the situation would have felt indicated insanity. To the last degree the boy was rude, insulting, and profane, particularly to his mother. Sometimes he was cynically polite to her. He alternated between abusing her for trying to circumvent his desire to serve his country and accusing her of wanting to get rid of him. He dramatized himself as the family pariah. Several times, arriving home in the early hours of the morning, he entered his mother's room, rudely awakened her, and violently berated her. The very flexible schedule of meal hours and bedtime was completely disregarded.

The mother took it all pretty well in her stride. She did several times "dress him down" soundly, but all in all she did not respond too aggressively nor did her conduct reveal the saddened and crushed-to-earth mother. There were tears—shed privately. However, she could never quite believe that she had nursed a viper at her breast.

The day came when the mother signed the consent and the youngster took the oath of enlistment into the Army. From that instant on he was a totally changed boy. During the short period of time before reporting to camp he treated his mother with natural consideration and affectionate regard. Later, for a three-hour break between trains and on a short furlough, mother and son had good times together. For both, these are happy memories which will never be erased.

This youngster has served for almost three years and his record is sound and good. No Congressional medals, but there have been things his mother prized more highly. With considerable difficulty the boy successfully completed special technical training. For the first time in his life he finished something. Perhaps an index to his character is furnished by the fact that voluntarily he relinquished his leave so that a boy who needed it more than he could go home. Yet, from time to time he is very homesick.

He writes perhaps not as frequently as his mother and sisters would like, but he writes happily, interestingly and wholeheartedly. His Army work during the war took him back and forth across the Pacific, and when he was on the Coast he telephoned home. Recently he acquired a girl and, judging from the picture he sent home, she is pretty and wholesome. Sometimes he gives his mother not too unsound advice about herself and various family matters. Occasionally he is quite explicit and mature in suggestions to his father. Obviously he has grown up.

So you see, the mother won. Immaturity was vanquished. After all, in spite of unfavorable and opposing conditions in the home, a hothouse of immaturity, she has produced a man. Whatever mistakes he may make in his future, and doubtless he will make many, he will meet them upstandingly and do his level best to retrieve their consequences. I predict he will be able to take it on the chin without going down for the full count.

This situation was presented in some detail because there are many mothers who with little or no help from their husbands find it increasingly difficult to keep their sights up to the aims of real motherhood. For the sake of the children and the nation, may they refuse steadfastly to yield to the temptation to descend into momism with its threat of immaturity and insecurity.

CHAPTER V

MOM TYPES

Seldom can the silver cord be identified as an obvious binding tie. It appears in many guises. And mom herself is a protean actress. Depending on degree and kind, there are many varieties of moms, but for convenience they can be grouped into seven basic classifications—the common garden variety of mom, the "self-sacrificing" mom, the "ailing" mom, the "pollyanna" mom; the "protective" mom, the "pretty-addlepate" mom, and the "pseudo-intellectual" mom. The distinctions are largely one of approach; the results invariably are the same.

The common garden variety of mom takes no end of trouble and spares herself no pains in selecting clothes for her grown-up children. She supervises the cut of their hair, the selection of their friends and companions, their sports, and their social attitudes and opinions. By and large she does all their thinking for them. By such solicitude I don't mean mature, wise guidance, but dominance—sometimes hard and arbitrary, more often soft, persuasive, and somewhat devious. Least common is direct admonition—"I won't let you have that suit." "Don't bring that rough boy, Jack, into this house again." "I won't allow you to play football." Most frequent is the method of indirection in which in some way the child is made to feel that mom is hurt and trying ever so hard to conceal that hurt. The soft method is infinitely more successful in blocking manifestations of youthful independence of thought and action.

A girl of 15, shopping with her mother for clothes, fixed her eyes and her heart upon one of the dresses on display. Perhaps it was not the wisest selection in the shop, but it was inexpensive, serviceable, and suitable. Said mom, "Of course, you can have it if you insist, darling, but I know you won't be as happy with it as you will be with that lovely gray one, and I would be just a wee bit disappointed. I gave up my bridge to come with you and help you buy just the nicest dress." Joan "decided" on the gray dress.

I know one mom who wooed her fourteen-year-old son away from a somewhat G.I. haircut to the more poetic one she wanted without uttering a single word of protest. It was only necessary for her not to try too hard to conceal a few soft sighs and the tears in her eyes when she gazed (as she frequently did) at her boy's favorite haircut. It is interesting to record that, years before, this same mom had delayed the shearing of her son's flaxen curls for more than a year, even though it involved frequent battles with her husband who had heard other boys refer to his son as "that sissy."

Another mom broke up her son's friendship with a robust youngster by being plaintively sweet about it, but invariably having a "sick headache" each time Bill and

Jack engaged in rough-and-tumble play just outside the house.

A third mom lured her son from football to tennis by being discovered in tears when the boy returned from practice. After much persuasion she reluctantly admitted she lived in daily terror that he would be injured. The final touch was the gift of a fine tennis racquet, "so that when you play, dear, you will be playing for mom."

So, too, may adolescent opinions and attitudes be directed into the channels of "momistic" thinking, not by explanation, discussion, or argument, but by questionable and camouflaged techniques. Whether they realize it or not, moms discourage self-attitudes and self-opinions not because they may be erroneous, but because they are behavior warnings that the son or daughter is growing up and beginning to move away from the maternal orbit. This is why mom blights maturing thought and emotion. Even though she may not know why she does it, the disastrous result for the children is not mitigated by her ignorance.

The "self-sacrificing" mom when hard pressed may admit hesitatingly that perhaps she does look "played out" and is actually a bit tired, but she chirps brightly, "What of it?" She does not say so, but the implication is that she does not care how she looks or feels, for in her heart there is the "unselfish" joy of service. From dawn until late at night she finds her happiness in doing for her children. The house belongs to them. It must be "just so"; the meals on the minute, hot and tempting.

Food is available at all hours. No need to stop at "Tony's Diner" for a snack, for even if it is well after midnight the opening of the house door is very likely to be the signal for mom's voice, calling sweetly, "Jack, there is some milk and a tray of sandwiches I fixed for you in the icebox." No buttons missing from garments in this orderly house. Everything is in its proper place. Mom knows where it is. Uncomplainingly, gladly, she puts things where they belong after the children have strewn them about, here, there, and everywhere. The service is almost continuous. The trail between the rooms of the house, down to the cellar, up to the attic is constantly and hurriedly traversed by mom's willing feet. Anything the children need or want mom will cheerfully get for them. It is the perfect home. No wonder, then, even though she tries bravely to conceal it, mom is a "little hurt" if her kiddies, twelve, fourteen, and eighteen years old, do not spend practically all their free time in this perfect home. Of course, she would not voice it, but deep down in her heart, she whispers: "Where else can they find what I give them here?"

For sons and daughters who pass from such conditions to everyday "give-and-take" living (civilian or military) it is like stepping from a delightfully warm shower, run for you by mom when you are in a hurry, into a bone-chilling cold mountain lake. The Army and Navy keep orderly houses, too, but the order must be kept by the men who live in them. There are inspections, unpleasant for those whose persons, clothing, and equipment are not shipshape. Failure of each man to make his individual contribution to the general order by keeping himself, his quarters, and his belongings neatly policed calls forth punishment, KP or even worse for the offender and sometimes for the whole group. This does not increase the popularity of the culprit. Mom is too far away to put things in order.

Then there is the "ailing" mom who has given all her strength in bearing her children. Now in middle life she is pitifully frail, often "too weak" to raise a finger. The doctor says there is no organic disease, "she just isn't very strong." Not that she ever speaks of it; yet somehow even the neighbors know of her sadly spent condition. The children of such moms always know. Some of them know it bitterly and resentfully, but invariably there is at least one child, usually a daughter, sometimes a son, who knows it lovingly and pityingly. Around this child the silver cord is drawn taut. Why not? It is a life for a life—fair enough. After all, there should be great happiness in giving all for her who gave so unstintingly in bringing the child into the world and caring for it when it was helpless.

Psychiatrists know there is a catch. It is not a fair bargain. We have seen too many broken and frightened men and women, after death had taken away the "invalid" mom. It was too late for them to re-enter the lists of life. The silver cord had been drawn so taut that all other personal and social threads had snapped. Under the memory of love and self-sacrifice, there is a deep and dark well of lost opportunity which now is beginning to stir, threatening to flood into consciousness, carrying with it bitterness and hatred against the mom who broke them upon the wheel of her own selfish life.

In the armed services I have seen men not able to perform their duties, or perhaps going through the motions robot-like, haunted and harassed by memory pictures of an "ailing" mom who "needs" them as her letters amply testify. Only a very few of these men could maintain their morale at a high level. Some of them escaped back to the servitude of love by the psychoneurotic route, sometimes labeled "situational" when the psychiatrist felt that the anxiety produced by the home situation was greater than the personality of the particular soldier could bear.

Sometimes the silver cord softly knits together the family circle in complete "harmony" and "happiness." Blessedly, arguments are checked and the hasty word is stilled in its utterance by the "pollyanna" mom: "Hush, children, we love each other too much to quarrel." It is very beautiful, like a waxen flower contrived by a skilled craftsman. It is *too* beautiful and *too* artificial. The house is *too* much of a sanctuary from the rough contest of down-to-earth everyday living. Failing to find a comparable peaceful haven in the outside world, it is quite likely that one or more of the brood will remain in or return to this happy home, forever enwombed.

The everyday world is an arena of contention, sometimes mounting to physical belligerency. Opinions strongly presented, passionately defended, and aggressively attacked by those who believe contrariwise is a natural part of the democratic way of life. Calm, detached, logical discussion belongs to scientists. Emotional emphasis gives strength, purpose, and direction to public movements of all kinds, and gets things done. Purely logical intellectual debates do not inspire great movements and a solely intellectual civilization would become pallid and emasculated, probably perishing from inanition.

In military life, particularly during war, there is much contention. Every platoon or squad is a forum of energetic, argumentative discussions, vigorously upheld and vehemently attacked. Furthermore, men are on edge, and words may be readily enough enforced and punctuated with fists. Even if there are no differences of opinion, still there are the animal spirits of the men, the absence of many emotional outlets afforded by civilian life—and the consequent tensions are released in numerous rough-and-tumble exhibitions. The boy from the pollyanna home is at a disadvantage—nonplussed. Either he learns to fit in and learns quickly, or else he is in danger of being regarded as "soft" or "queer" or "high-hat," and like as not he will be on the receiving end of rough practical jokes.

The "protective" mom no doubt is activated by sincere, although sentimentally immature considerations. She unerringly and usually deftly inserts herself as a protective barrier between the children, or more often between one child and justly merited censure from the father or from the other children. The unfortunate victim of such solicitude is doomed to find out that the personal and social conditions of adult life swiftly and casually nullify the emotional bond of protective security from deserved blame given in childhood.

Sometimes the protective mom wages her defensive warfare openly. This may partake of all the qualities of melodrama, the "outraged" mother treading the summits of histrionic art with the limelight shining down upon her and her "innocent" child, incidentally magnifying his ego and diminishing his chances of growing up.

Much more pernicious than the melodrama is the silent pact between mom and her child. While the child is being punished, she pursues a policy of noninterference. The child knows all too well the lines of the last act of this familiar comedy. He will be gathered into mom's arms, solaced and petted and given a largess of emotional and material rewards for having been so "brave." Thus, gently and expertly, mom binds the child to herself with the silver cord. Each binding further diminishes the child's chances of ever being able to free himself.

Neither in civilian life in its business or other affairs, in family life and, in fact, in all personal and social relationships nor in the Army is it possible to go on very long without incurring censure. One may slide out of blame for a time, but to balance this moratorium, there comes to every human being a certain measure of unmerited blame. Unless the child has learned to face the consequences of his acts, then as an adult his ego will be frequently and badly bruised. He is likely to be crushed in his personality, or else it becomes twisted with distrust and suspicion.

There is a mom I think of as the "pretty-addlepate." She would be amusing if she did not do so much damage. Certainly she makes no conscious effort to bind her children to her side. Generally she is away from them, bent on pleasure not strictly maternal. She is of the tribe of Narcissus. She follows an elaborate cult of beauty with lengthy rituals of clothing, cosmetics, and perfumes, hairdos, dieting, exercise, massage, etc. She achieves the result she strives for. She is pleasing to the eye; and she is very pleasing in the eyes of her children. When she bends over them before leaving for a party, all sweetness and grace and beauty, delicately perfumed, the children are entranced by the vision—"Mother is so lovely and smells so sweet." The odor unfortunately comes in bottles, and is not the mother odor. No harm in all this and it may even be commendable, but as far as the addlepate I have in mind goes, this is about all the children see of her. She is rarely visible, even to her own children, unless she looks and smells "just so." For her children, at least the female children, the cult of beauty becomes a shrine at which to worship. A little girl I know bursts into hysterical weeping if there is even a remote suggestion that any other woman is as beautiful as her mother or any little girl as pretty as she. For the sons, the ideal of womanhood engraven on their personalities is one in which physical pulchritude is the important component.

A rose by any other name will never smell so sweet to them.

There is another mom who is as serious as the addle-pate is frivolous and as useless. She is the "pseudo-intellectual" mom. She is forever taking courses and attending lectures, not seriously studying one subject and informing herself thoroughly about it, but gathering a few blossoms of "knowledge" here and there. One month it is mental hygiene, the next economics. Astrology succeeds Greek architecture, and nursery schools follow phrenology. To her children her owlish, heavily rimmed spectacles are as fascinating as the golden sleek hair-do of the addlepate. The mind behind the spectacles usually is just as immature as the one under the expertly tinted tresses and just as incapable of pointing the way for children in the direction of intelligent, well-rounded, unfettered maturity.

The thoroughgoing mom is not enthusiastic about her children having private lives. Should a child be a bit quiet—"just thinking, mom"—a worried frown appears upon her face and she begins to probe: "Is anything worrying you?" "Did anyone do anything mean to my boy?" "I know you would like to tell mom. You wouldn't want to have any secrets from mom. That would make her unhappy."

The portrait of our social lives is composed not only of our public and company behavior, but also of the thinking that goes on in the hidden recesses of our minds. There should be a free but balanced in-and-out flow in our thinking. If the mind is a closed citadel it is not good. It is equally detrimental to mature emotional and social existence if the mind has never acquired the art of quiet thinking, pro and con planning, even ruminating and daydreaming a bit. If there is merely a very coarse sieve between the inner self and the outside world, then that which is trying to shape itself in the mind comes through almost at once and usually in such incomplete form that it is uninteresting and almost never a contribution to the social scheme.

Sometimes, and naturally enough, a potentially adequate mother falls to the level of a mom because of defects and handicaps in her children. The defect may be present at birth or appear soon after, like paralysis due to a birth injury or feeble-mindedness, or it may be acquired as in infantile paralysis. If a mother has produced a baby that is not right in its body or mind, the baby is a constant insult to her ego. Unconsciously, she may attempt to soothe her own hurt by extreme solicitude and over-attention to the child. Should the child's handicap be acquired, as when it is stricken and crippled by polio or some other dread disease, then the bottomless wells of maternal pity are deeply stirred. I have seen fine mothers dangerously tip the balance of their former good judgment and common sense by sympathy for a child reduced by a long and painful illness. In her desire to make up for what has been endured and suffered, the convalescence becomes a spoiling time and the youngster's opportunity for climbing back to his former level of maturing behavior is lost. The dice become heavily loaded against the chances of acquiring full emotional and social growth.

The life records of many of those physically handicapped in childhood or even in adult life are golden records of adequate and successful adjustment. Among them is the life history of a great President. These men and women could not have struggled to the peaks unless their mothers had given them that first long, strong boost, teaching them to stand on their own legs, even though those legs were crippled.

On one of my trips for the Air Forces, I met a remarkable young woman, although I feel sure she would object to that description. Her husband, an Air Forces captain, had been killed and she was running a hostess house for overseas patients in the hospital compound. She had not had any children, which was unfortunate since she was a real mother without any momish nonsense about her. The hostess house was a home, friendly and happy, but each man who came there was expected to try to be a grown-up man, with definite responsibilities and obligations as well as fun and privileges. The men flocked to the house and brought their wives. Together with the hostess they planned their futures.

I noticed that the young woman always wore a simple black ribbon around her neck and her voice was just a trifle husky. One of the officers explained that the ribbon concealed a tube inserted into the larynx, through which she breathed. As far as I know, she is the only child who is known to have survived after closure of the larynx as a result of streptococcic throat infection.

Mrs. A. talked freely to me about it. As a child she attempted to use her difficulty in order to escape doing unpleasant things, particularly reciting lessons which she had neglected to prepare. However, her mother gently but firmly blocked the childish attempts at evasion and skillfully foiled the youngster's efforts to capitalize and dramatize her throat injury. One brother, a few years older, was very helpful. He gave "shows" to which he admitted the neighborhood children at a penny a head (two pennies for front row seats) to see his sister take off the ribbon and breathe through the tube.

One can have little patience with those moms who worry constantly and needlessly about the health of healthy children: "Don't play so hard, you are not very strong." "Don't get wet, your lungs are a little weak." "Don't run, you might trip and break your ankle."

The average boy resents such oversolicitude, yet if mom persists, the silver cord eventually will be securely woven into the emotional life of the youngster. Self-preservation is the strongest of human instincts. Undue solicitude on mom's part is harmful.

I have seen many boys and girls severely penalized in life by an early canalization of interest in health. In the Army, not only was the normal fear of war greatly magnified for these boys, but innumerable other fears were added—fear of catching cold after sweating in drill or

maneuvers; fear that the chow had been carelessly prepared and was overdone or even that it contained dirt or
infection; fear of being injured in combat practice and
so on, until each day from dawn until night was fear-
ridden.

During the war I witnessed many leave-takings. Some
of the women staged emotional exhibitions which would
have put the immortal Bernhardt to shame. Once on a
station platform in Hartford I saw a woman shrieking
in hysterical grief and anguish, clinging to her son as the
train was about to leave. The husband with the tears
streaming down his face had to separate forcibly mother
and son. Two younger children screamed in terror. As
the boy boarded the train, I heard him repeating—"Please,
mom."

Often I have seen real mothers take leave of their sons.
No hilarious laughter, but a few little joking remarks
keenly appreciated by the family party. Bobby-sox sister
dividing admiring glances between her brother and a
handsome young ensign waiting for his train. The kid
brother entranced by a tall paratrooper. Father feeling
very proud but serious, trying to smile but not making
a very good job of it. After a hasty kiss from his sister, a
solid handshake from his father, and a hug and a big
kiss from a bravely smiling mother with a jaunty "Be
seeing you," the soldier marched into the car, straight-
backed and strong. Surely that mother was entitled to a
few quiet tears when the train was out of sight.

The sons of both mothers and moms were killed in

battle. Somehow I think the heavy hand of death was kinder to mothers than to moms. The grief of the mother is deep, but it is a quiet and dignified grief. Few people see the tears she sheds. By the bright lights of motherhood she has done her best for her son. She still has a job in life. She adds a bit to what she is doing for the soldiers. She senses the sympathy and support of her friends. She carries on. Her son would want it that way.

The grief of the unfortunate mom is apt to be wild and unrestrained. She may follow various rituals. *His* room is to be kept locked and only she may enter. No one but she may touch *his* things. Often she dashes away from the dinner table in a paroxysm of grief. Or perhaps she is too sad to come to dinner at all. Her friends are afraid to express sympathy. Timidly her husband or a friend suggests doing a little war work—"it might make it easier for you." Tragically, she turns upon them, "Don't talk to me of war, helping something which took my boy away from me." She cannot "carry on" even for her own family. Truly she is miserable, perhaps the more so because of a vague feeling within her that she did not do a good job for her son and now it is too late to retrieve her mistakes.

I have sketched word profiles of only a few of the many varieties of moms and have examined only a few of many silver cords. Moms have one thing in common, varying in degree but the same in kind. They hold on to their children unduly long and almost never willingly relinquish their grasp. They fail to prepare them for independent, mature adult lives. Some silver cords are longer and more flexible than others, but in one thing they are alike—both ends are firmly affixed, one to the child, the other to the mom.

CHAPTER VI

WHAT MAKES A MOM?

The causes of moms are just about as numerous as the types of silver cords moms finally use to bind their children to them. But again the one word "immaturity" gives the overall answer.

In most cases, a mom is a mom because she is the immature result of a mom. Her momism had its foundation in the fact that she herself was raised by an immature parent. The pattern for her life was set long before she knew it or could do anything about it. Actually, she doesn't want to be a mom. Actually, in most cases, she doesn't realize that she is a mom, and would resent it if she were accused. She believes that she is being everything a real mother should be to her children. Didn't her mother use the same tactics?

Immaturity breeds immaturity, and so goes the vicious cycle. Hundreds of case histories could be cited, but I use the following example because my knowledge of it extends over three generations—grandmother to mother and now to daughter who in her turn is imposing momism on her young son. The grandmother was the garden variety type of mom and when her daughter grew up she, too, became the dominant mom who in turn prevented her daughter from growing up. When the daughter found a husband, she entered marriage without the slightest knowledge of what constituted a mature married life —even to the point of not knowing how children were conceived or born. She, like her mom before her, had been told that sex was degrading, horrible, and entirely a man-made and man-enjoyed affair. It was something a woman had to put up with in exchange for a home. She knew nothing of family finances and home-running —her mom had always taken care of such things and had picked out her clothes and her friends for her as well.

After six years her first marriage ended in a Reno divorce. She has since remarried, and has a young son. The boy, now seven years old, is fast becoming a mom's child. Unfortunately, the girl's mom is still living, so the youngster is feeling the effects of double momism—his mom and his mother's mom. My one hope is that the father, unfortunately a man overly interested in his business affairs, some day soon will take a hand in the raising of his son.

Lack of interest on the part of the husband often brings latent momism to the fore. A woman, left saddled with all the responsibilities of raising a family without help from her mate, naturally hates to see her children, the one thing she has left, grow away from her. She treats them as possessions rather than individuals who have a right to their own lives. Unconsciously, she hates to think ahead to the time when she will be alone—her children gone and her husband too interested in his business, his social life and his golf to be a companion. Quite naturally, she falls into the pitfalls of momism. They are "her" children, not "their" children; and she means to keep them as such. Generally her affections are centered on the youngest boy of the family—in him she sees the companionship she has failed to get from her husband.

Sexual frustration, likewise, can be the seed from which a mom grows. Never having been able to reach the heights of sexual satisfaction with her husband, something in her life is missing and the lack is an insult to her ego. As recompense, she subconsciously grasps at the one remaining means of inflating that ego—her children. Generally, she becomes the "self-sacrificing" mom, for by doing so her ego is not only gratified by the fact that she can hold her children to her but that she can enjoy the practice of self-pity.

Some moms once were mothers—mothers who slipped into the ways of momism later in life because of the lack of attention on the part of the husband or because of the lack of normal sex life. This type of delayed mom shows up quite often in families of three or four children where the youngest child arrived fairly late in life. With the older children mom was a good mother. She was young and could throw off the fact that her husband paid little or no attention to her. She had other interests—her house, community affairs, her friends, her children. However, by the time the youngest child begins his formative years the mother, perhaps in her late thirties, has begun to tire under the full responsibility of running the family. She begins to want and require companionship; her outside interests are dwindling. Under these conditions, it takes a strong mother not to fall into the pitfall of feeling that her last born, particularly if it is a boy, is hers. Here is a chance for her to have companionship in later life, here is her chance as the boy grows older to shift some of her responsibilities, here in effect is a chance to make a husband out of her son. Some mothers recognize the symptoms and, like the real mothers they are, fight it. Others slip and another mom is added to the rolls.

And far from the least of the mom causes, because it is the fertile soil in which the seeds of momism grow, is our social system and our way of life. Pretty much everything we do—socially, politically, educationally—glorifies mom and praises her "self-sacrifice" and her "giving her life for her children." In her community, a mom is likely to be judged the ideal mother while the real mother often goes unnoticed—unnoticed because she does not wear her motherhood on her sleeve. As a nation, we are inclined to take things at their face value without delving into the results. Instead of censuring mom for her shortcomings, we encourage her with misplaced adoration. But more on this later.

In any case, fortunately, a mature young woman seldom becomes a mom. Maturity and momism seldom live together. Show me an immature bride and I feel safe in saying that she has eighty chances out of a hundred of becoming a mom. If she has no children, she will do her level best to exercise all the tricks of momism on her husband, particularly if he, too, is immature.

CHAPTER VII

MOMS IN PANTS

Yes, sometimes pop is a mom. The "joys" of momism are by no means reserved for the female of the species. Sometimes pop may be so much of a mom that he can only be distinguished by the fact that he wears trousers—in these days scarcely a sure mark of sex.

Again, usually the metamorphosis of the male parent into a mom also had its beginnings when he was a child and had a mom. As is the way with moms, she left him dangling on the limb of emotional immaturity in adult life. This was, indeed, a precarious perch, so naturally he reached out desperately for some source of strength and support. Even though he did not realize it, this was the principal motivation of his marriage.

Young women, and perhaps particularly young women who have the markings of fine and adequate wives and mothers, are rarely calm, dispassionate, and detached concerning marriage. Following the ancient biological law of the female, they are strongly moved emotionally. The maternal instinct is the potent driving force. The helpless immature type of male too often makes a deep appeal to such a woman's budding sense of maternity. Frequently marriage results from the mixture of these two elements.

Then the wife finds she has married a child-adult. For a time the situation may be intriguing, but soon it begins to pall. Particularly is this true when children begin to arrive. They provide a much more satisfactory answer to the call of maternity than does a big hulking fellow of 25 or 30 who always wants to be babied. A thoughtful observer once remarked that a successful wife should be wife, mistress, mother, and child, but the formula must be properly compounded. The role of rubbing his "poor, tired back" and endlessly soothing his ruffled feelings, that is, being his mom, is scarcely a substitute for the full contribution of the male to the marriage—as husband, lover, father, and child. So the immature husband, failing to find another mom in his wife, may engage earnestly in the business of being a mom to his children. Possibly it is the only available sop to his ego. For the wife who is trying sincerely to be a genuine mother, a mom for a husband poses a problem which can be solved only by increasing vigilance and thoughtful planning. The more firmly the wife-mother tries to anchor the children to the moorings of emotional and social stability, the harder the husband-mom seems to strive to pull them away into the whirlpool of emotional and social instability. Even when the wife is strong and determined, the husband is still the father of their children and therefore has a certain amount of nuisance value.

There are many techniques of being a male mom, all of them easy and pleasant. For instance, it is simple to curry the children's favor by never punishing them. Thus the mother acquires the reputation of being the ogress, the stern disciplinarian, while the father is thought of as "nice" and never "tough." If a mother is attempting to teach a child the value of money by having him manage his allowance and keep within it, the father can torpedo the effort by slipping the youngster extra dimes and quarters. The child will beam upon him.

The father may enact the role of mom by taking open issue with the wife in the presence of the children concerning some matter—let us say, the relative merits of preparing the next day's school lessons versus going to the corner drug store and playing the pin-ball machine. The mother is put between the devil and the deep blue sea. If she declines to accept the challenge the children take one backward step from maturity. If she accepts, there is the likelihood of a quarrel. Then, even if she triumphs, there is the danger that the children will feel that she is bullying the father and this is particularly likely if he accepts defeat with "patient resignation." Above all things, children do not wish their mother to be a bullying female.

Like the female mom, the male one may be a past master in the momish art of using words sparingly and depending more for effect upon nuances of voice, bearing, gestures, and facial expressions. The children may come to him seeking an appeal from the mother's rulings. His words, "Maybe you should do as your mother wishes," may be fair enough, but his tired, patient voice and air of sad resignation speak all too plainly: "You know how it is. I understand and wish I could help you. I *am* sorry."

The male mom has an unusually good opportunity when before the children he succeeds in "needling" his wife into an expression of lack of sympathy for endlessly reiterated woes. Children cannot be expected to realize that their mother is for the moment tired from thinking, planning, and helping three or four normal children grow up and that for once the whining of a large, hopelessly immature adult child is more than she can stand. All the children see is the immediate picture. "Poor dad, he is tired, his head aches, and his feet hurt, and mother is pretty tough about it." It is altogether likely that a half-grown daughter will steal softly to the couch and gently rub his head.

More devious and much more threatening is the technique by which the immature father courts his own daughter, usually a girl in her middle 'teens. The fact that he does not realize the extent of the damage he is doing the child does not save it from being emotionally an incestuous relationship. Having exhausted his wife's possibilities as a substitute for his own mom, he turns to his daughter and drains the emotional reserves she is beginning to accumulate. Appealingly he turns to her at the most critical and vulnerable time of her life—a time when she is apt to be highly romantic in her thinking and feeling about older men, when her father is her hero, when her maternal instincts are beginning to put forth tender shoots. Her ego is flattered by her father's attention and she is easily wooed and won. Between her and her father there is an unspoken pact which excludes the mother. The father lays his troubles upon her small but receptive lap, usually vaguely and sadly intimating that mother does not understand. The daughter has found her mission in life—loving and helping dad. She is only too eager to fetch and carry for him, take off his shoes, and give him his aspirin, stroke his tired brow, sit quietly at his side for hours, figuratively and sometimes actually holding his hand.

In the meantime, the child's chances of achieving maturity are being rapidly diminished. If and when she marries, she will find a dilemma; and there is a serious danger of the marriage being impaled upon the horn of her father-determined emotional infantilism. If she marries an equally immature man, they will live in a doll's house of emotional and social disorder which will always be in imminent danger of crashing about her ears. If she marries a grown-up man, he will soon tire of the "little mother" who is little else. If she has children, she is an exceedingly likely candidate for the ranks of momism.

When a male parent succeeds in psychologically seducing his own daughter, he has attained the ultimate in male momism. The only comparison is the achievement of the female mom who has so successfully solicited her son that he renounces the ways of men and the evils of the flesh, remaining at her side until the end of her days, and emotionally much longer—until the end of his days.

If there has been a divorce, then the male mom does not yield to the female in the accuracy of his vengeful marksmanship. The post-divorce territory is littered with the remains of his ex-wife's reputation and her standing with her children.

The male mom is adept at dramatizing his divorced status. When his children are visiting him he is histrionically expert in depicting in dignified fashion his sad and lonely lot in life. The children carry away the picture of a miserable, unhappy father wending his dreary way homeward from work and spending night after night in his cheerless room alone but for the company of his melancholy thoughts. Actually, as in many cases I know, these male moms do not spend night after night cloistered with their sad and lonely reflections. When they do come home, the night is apt to have turned into the morning hours and often they are pleasantly accompanied by memories of alcoholically bedewed and immature assignations.

Because the two contracting parties in a marriage happen to be a mature man and a mature woman does not necessarily insure the permanence and success of the marriage. Nevertheless, such a marriage definitely has a much better chance of survival than if one of the contracting parties is decidedly immature. It is not easy for an adult to live in a close emotional relationship with a child, and it is notably hard to do it within the confines of matrimony. There is a somewhat better chance of success if the husband is the mature partner, particularly if he is very mature. I know of a few such men who "carry along" child-wives fairly well and maintain at least a semblance of family life. Of course, the children do not escape the psychological penalty entirely, and there is always the danger that a son and sometimes a daughter will absorb the father's devotion and assume care of the mother, but will not have his strength of character and the inner resources by which he retains his individuality. Then the son or daughter becomes a victim to the draining demands of momism.

If it is the wife who is mature, the marital situation is more complicated and difficult. The male of the species still retains some vestiges of former dominance and superiority, or at least he wants to be credited with still having these traits. Girls, even those girls who are destined to become moms, do not visualize a husband who will be a wishy-washy weakling. Like their mature sisters, they want to marry strong men, or at least, they think they do. In the ego of every male, no matter how immature, there is at least a trace of the desire to be strong, protective and even dominant in the role of husband. Too immature to satisfy this abortive ego-wish or anything approaching it on an adult level, he is reduced to childish methods of asserting male superiority. One device is to insist that his wife join him in doing the things he likes to do while refusing to participate with her in any of her interests.

I know a husband, a beefy, good-natured fellow, who is "just a harmless boy at heart." Unfortunately, in addition to preparing him adequately for the role of perpetual playboy his mom also endowed him with great wealth. So he is at liberty to pursue his one absorbing interest in life—horses. It is only fair to add that he is "fond" of his wife and "proud" of her. I suspect that without her he would be quite helpless.

He would be deeply hurt if his wife did not accompany him to the nightly gatherings of the crowd with which he rides to hounds and pursues other equine matters. He not only wants her to go with him, but he wants her to enjoy herself. This is not altogether easy since the crowd is quite "horsey" and she is not. Furthermore, alcoholic inebriation and "pawing" of females by the males and vice versa are the accepted customs. However, the wife goes to the parties good-naturedly enough and, since she has accumulated a small stock of equine lore, she does not disgrace her husband too much. Of course, the charter members of the crowd are mildly sorry for him.

One day I encountered the couple and they asked my advice. On the somewhat casual theory of turn about being fair play, I suggested that occasionally the husband accompany his wife in the pursuit of her interests and try to understand and enjoy them. Somewhat sadly he agreed.

Some months later I saw them again and inquired as to progress. The wife remarked: "Oh, we decided to go back to the old way. Jim gets pretty tired out in the open all day with the horses and we feel that at night he must relax."

Later I picked up some of the details of the experiment in developing mutual interests and pieced them together.

The man's first attempt was to go with his wife to a private viewing of the paintings of several famous modern artists. The setting was good. The paintings were neither realistic nor superrealistic, just fine art. Lobster and champagne were served. However, there were no paintings of horses.

It seems that Jim's contribution to the viewing was to partake liberally of the champagne and lobster and, in respect to the paintings, to emit a series of unintelligible noises, halfway between a college cheer and the neighing of a happy horse, that were meant to be sounds of approval and interest. Naturally the other guests did not understand Jim's good intentions and were surprised and amused.

The wife was not discouraged and tried another exhibition of paintings. This time Jim gazed at the paintings in dark and gloomy silence. Probably it was an improvement on the first reaction since it might have passed for interest too deep for words.

The final episode occurred when Mrs. Jim succeeded in gathering for dinner a distinguished group of men and women, several of the men being experts in world politics. The stage was set for an evening of informing and fascinating conversation. Jim's participation consisted of a few very emphatic "yeses," one weak "no," and the display of an amazing feat of memory in which he recited rapidly and without a single error the track records of a dozen famous horses. Even though it was totally malapropos, one of the gentlemen felt that as guest he should try to be responsive. Unfortunately, he knew as little about race horses as did his host about international politics, so for a few minutes it appeared to be somewhat doubtful whether Dumbarton Oaks was a house in Washington where an important international economic-political conference was held or a good "mud" horse with a chance of winning the Derby, should it be held on a rainy day. So ended the experiment.

The moral is this: If a husband's interests are single-tracked, because of necessary close attention to his profession or business, then a mature wife will be able gradually to improve the situation. She will operate on two fronts—familiarizing herself with at least the outlines of her husband's work so that she can discuss it intelligently with him, and also taking advantage of opportunities to open up new and diverting interests for and with her husband. If, however, an immature husband uses his husbandly role to enforce his limited interests upon his wife to the exclusion of all else, there is little to be done.

If it is the wife who is immature, her fund of conversation is apt to be inexhaustible but still quite limited—a wealth of words but a poverty of ideas. After all, no matter how gaily the patter runs on, conversation restricted to dresses and hats, beauty creams, and reducing exercises is likely to pall. Of course, they can talk about the children. Now between a mature husband and wife, children, particularly their own children, provide a topic of interesting discussion which can never be exhausted.

In the course of years, husbands and wives together may explore almost the entire range of human knowledge. At some point everything from anthropology to zoology, from finger painting to great masterpieces of art, from the nursery school movement to the relative merits of the college preceptorial system, touches on the past, present, or future lives of "Junior" or "Sister." However, if the slightest objection on the husband's part to some particularly overt practice of the momish art transforms the wife into a raging tigress, wrathfully defending herself and her young with slashing verbal fang and claw, or if the husband's mildest reproof is a signal for a loud wail of anguish or a long, stony silence, then perhaps, after all, it would be just as well if the husband returned to the editorial or sports page and the wife resumed reading her fashion magazine.

One of the meanest weapons used by the immature husband in his petty tyrannies to bolster his ego and compel attention from a grown-up wife is money. Even though the wife is provident in the distribution of the available money, still every penny must be counted out for each separate item of expenditure. This husband manages to keep his wife in more or less complete ignorance of his income and material possessions. Some husbands reverse the process, handing over every penny of their earnings to their wives, who allot the amounts necessary for the husband's current expenses. Sometimes, when the income is small and the wife a good manager, this is a sensible arrangement. However, it is an earmark of immaturity if the husband does it for the sake of the unconscious satisfaction he derives from coaxing an extra dollar from his wife—satisfaction, since it revives the boyhood pattern of wheedling money from mom.

The correspondingly immature wife usually does not want to know the details of income, unless it is quite large and she fears she is not getting all she should have. Otherwise, she "goes to town," spending for herself and the children with gay and wanton disregard of the Dickensian warning as to the balance that should be maintained between income and expenditure and its effect in terms of human happiness or woe.

I have known some immature husbands who exhibited an unbelievable amount of jealousy of their wives' friends, including women friends. When friends call, even though the wife gives the husband the opportunity of remaining out of sight, he insists on wandering in and out of the room, indicating by his manner, if not by words, that an early termination of the visit would be highly satisfactory. In his childhood this kind of husband was jealous and resentful even toward his brothers and sisters, if they intruded into the inner sanctum of love which *only* he and mom occupied. Except in the romance of early youth, intense unreasoning jealousy is a hallmark of immaturity.

Often child-wives are "insanely" jealous. If so, they are apt to wield their jealousy as a double-edged sword, to intimidate their husbands and to rationalize their own unwise and dangerous clinging to their children. Sometimes, even without a shred of real evidence against her husband, a wife may justify her absorption of her children because she must protect her "helpless kiddies" from that "terrible woman."

There is a type of child-husband, who in social gatherings, and apropos of nothing at all, suddenly calls loudly across the room to his wife: "Pet, this cold weather reminds me of that time you were gypped and paid for two tons of coal instead of one." Or, "Darling, I picked up a copy of 'H' magazine today. It reminded me of the time you paid a year's subscription to a fellow who came to the door and said he was working his way through college, but we never got the magazine—remember?" Or, "Dear, do you remember the night your mother got tipsy on sherry and we had to take her home in a taxi?" Of course, the wife remembers. She could scarcely forget. She has been reminded publicly many, many times. The husband embarrasses the wife in this fashion because she was being listened to attentively by the company while he was being neglected. Immaturity craves attention, occupying the center of the stage whenever possible and resorting to any device at all to secure the spotlight. Furthermore, this husband does not want his wife to become interested in other people. He wants all her interest for himself. Conceivably, when he was a little boy and calling upon friends with his mother, if she seemed to be enjoying the adult conversation very much he would suddenly set up a howl, shrieking, "I wanna go home, mom."

Many immature husbands have anemic love affairs with

a long series of equally immature women. Although the affairs are bathed in sickly sentimentality, nothing very much seems to happen. There is a deal of sighing, some tender handholding, and sometimes a bit more. At times the husband enacts the role of being fatherly and protective. In turn the current woman plays the part of the mother, literally exuding mother love. For all the world, it is like two tots playing at being grown up. The affairs are not too deeply concealed from the wife. Perhaps she will understand that she must not become interested in other people and things. Her child-husband needs all her attention. Reminiscently, when a mother becomes a bit impatient at an annoying child, the child may say, "I love the lady next door more than I love you. I will go to see her and be her little boy. She will give me candy and cake."

When it comes to seeking the cooperation of an immature husband in the numerous matters which have to do with the welfare of the children, the wife and mother is faced with a dilemma not easy of solution. As far as the decisions go, it would be much more satisfactory if she made them herself, but if she does not make a pretense of asking the advice of her husband, then he is hurt. When an immature man is hurt he does not conceal it but wears it openly for all the world to see. He trails it through the home where his wound is freely displayed, morning, noon, and night. He might as well carry a signboard "Unfair to husbands."

Furthermore, the mother knows that there is a certain

stage in a boy's development when she cannot possibly be
the surrogate for her husband. At this age her son has
very definite ideas concerning femininity and the role of
women in this world. He wants to feel deeply chivalrous
toward his mother and he can scarcely think in terms of
chivalry about a competent executive. Therefore, it becomes necessary for the wife to "star" the father and
depend on his "wise" decisions, even if he is only a man
of straw. If the wife accomplishes this, she must still
elude the second horn of the dilemma.

The immature husband cannot make decisions on the
spot or anywhere near the spot. Either he is "too tired,"
"all worn out by a very tough day at the office," or "too
busy"—or the matter is so weighty that he will have
to "take time to think it over," intimating that women
are apt to be intuitive and illogical. This, irrespective of
the fact that the wife has presented the matter diplo-
matically at least a dozen times during the past two
months and, unless she knows one way or the other
right now, it will be too late for Jim to get the dinner
jacket for the senior high school "prom" tomorrow night.

While the immature husband adroitly evades making
final commitments about the children, he scans the horizon with an eagle eye for any flaws that may appear
in the results of the decisions his wife has had to make.
Although he carefully held aloof from expressing any
preference as to schools for the youngsters or else delivered an opinion as equally balanced for and against
as the campaign speeches of an adroit politician whose

chief concern is not to leave even the smallest loophole through which his constituents might vote against him, yet, whichever school his wife selects, public or private, the selection is sure to be wrong. When difficulties begin to appear, whether they be with algebra or the breaking down of the school bus, the immature husband explains kindly and judicially why the choice of "that school" was unwise.

Some of these husbands, too, are apt to offer panaceas for the problems of children, no matter what may be their gravity. Is Johnny having serious scholastic difficulties? Confidently he suggests goat's milk or arch supports. If it is Mary Ann, then by all means aesthetic dancing. It is the mom pattern. She saw to it that he would never learn how to make careful decisions. If as a child he was in trouble and unhappy, mom could be relied upon to produce a charm to "wish away" the unhappiness or trouble.

Fortunately, immature husbands almost never tell their sons "the facts of life." If they did the sons would certainly feel that sex was indeed a weird and strange thing, as it is for the immature.

When he is sick, the immature husband reaches the very nadir of childishness. Not that he is necessarily a more difficult patient for the wife to nurse than the average man who comes down with the sniffles or flu. In fact, often he is far less aggressive in his sickroom decorum. The average man is rarely a well-behaved patient, particularly if the illness is mild. Usually men do not accept illness nearly so well as women. They are more frightened and consequently much more irritable and demanding.

The mature wife takes such behavior in her strides. She knows or senses that sometimes even a mature man is a child and needs mothering.

The immature husband when he is sick is likely to be silently reproachful rather than vociferously complaining. Should the wife be a bit late with the medicine or should there be crumbs in the bed, he is inclined to indicate by his demeanor more than by his words that all is not as it should be. His wife would have to have a psychological blind spot indeed if she failed to observe the deeply hurt and neglected look in his eyes. If the children are noisy, he may bravely struggle out of bed and close the door—that is, if his wife is near by and can see him do it. When there is pain, there are apt to be courageously stifled little moans, rather than the bull-like roar of the average, normal, sick husband.

The illness re-animates the pattern of being sick as a child. Among his loveliest memories, not only subconsciously but often consciously, is the picture of mom's tender and devoted care when he was sick. Time has not dimmed the happy memory. His inarticulate reproaches of his wife are in direct ratio to the degree in which she falls short of the measure of mom.

I have sketched merely the outlines of a few of the

behaviorisms of immature husbands and wives. There are many more nuances of conduct which cannot be encompassed in a framework of written words. As childhood was the testing field upon which the lessons of maturity should have been learned, so is marriage the place for their practical application.

The joining together in wedlock does not make the contracting parties capable of living a mature married life, any more than sitting in an airplane makes a skillful aviator. The close relationship of marriage imposes such high emotional and social ideals that no husband or wife may hope to realize them fully. In fact, perfection is not desirable. However, child-wives and child-husbands fall so far short of minimal requirements and ordinary expectations that it is not even a near miss. They make a travesty of marriage.

Sometimes I have had to attend weddings which I did not enjoy. When the officiating clergyman solemnly announced, "If any man can show just cause, why they may not lawfully be joined together, let him now speak, or else hereafter forever hold his peace," I have often had the desire to say, "Stop! I know just cause why they may not be lawfully joined together. That young man (or young woman) cannot fulfill the conditions of the married state. He is in love with another woman and always will love her more than anything else in the world. It is she he will love and cherish and not this young woman who stands at his side."

Sometimes I could almost see the hand of mom,

whether she was living or dead, reach out and unclasp the hands which had been joined together. And I could almost hear her say, "You cannot have this man. He belongs to me. I know what is in his heart. I put it there. He is forever mine."

CHAPTER VIII

MOMS BY PROXY

The mom in the house need not be a parent. There are a number of moms by proxy who can do as much damage as a parental mom. I like to call them "mom surrogates," because they are substitutes and successors.

Grandmothers may have momish proclivities. However, unless they were moms themselves, they are not too serious and are apt to confine themselves to minor bribes, sly little efforts to discount parental authority, obvious and somewhat amusing conspiracies with the children, assisting them in evading responsibility for misbehavior. All in all, if these grandmomish, and sometimes grandpopish, tricks do not assume too large proportions, it is not too difficult for sensible parents who have a sense of humor to repair the effects of these raids.

The problem is more serious if the children have a mom. Then grandmom can join forces and sometimes pour reserves of material resources into the battle at critical times. The lone opponent, husband or wife, has to utilize superior tactical skill in order to hold the defensive line of maturity for the children. Sometimes a rich grandmom attempts and may succeed in overwhelming the thinly held position by a heavy barrage of unlimited spending money, sports model roadsters, aviation lessons, and luxurious private schools.

When grandmom is merely maintaining her interests in life and somewhat oddly expressing her love for her grandchildren by minor infractions of the maturity code, no great harm is done. However, if she is feeding a voracious emotional appetite, unsatiated when she was a mom, then grandmom is lethal.

Grandmother is also a "mother-in-law." If strongly inclined to momism, functioning in her dual capacity, she is indeed a sanguinary opponent of maturity for children. Her field of operation is large. If her son is the father, it is likely that during his childhood, he was deeply injected with the mom virus. Then she has her field day. Resenting the wife, the intruder and usurper who separated her from her boy, she strives mightily to erase any outcroppings of maturity appearing in him as the result of association with a mature partner. At the same time, she tries to line up the children against their mother: "Your mother is a lucky woman. She has just about everything—a wonderful husband, a fine house, and such beautiful and smart children. She is so well and strong and never seems to get tired. It makes me very happy to see her enjoying life so much. . . . I wish I could say the same for your father. Children, I am worried about him. He works so hard and looks so thin and white. I suppose he needs different food. Vegetables out of a can never did agree with him."

No detail of family life is too small to escape the

mother-in-law's eagle eye. I knew one mother-in-law who computed the value of each article her daughter-in-law purchased from bedroom slippers to a very occasional evening dress. She used her estimates with momish shrewdness and with propitious timing. When her son was in a rebellious mood about the curtailment of his personal expenditures because of the needs of the house and family, she might "casually" remark, "Bill, you could have had that camel's hair overcoat you wanted if Margery hadn't put so much money into that black party dress she wore just once this year."

When the wife is the daughter, the formula works in reverse order. Then the son-in-law is placed in an unflattering category and the daughter is a "poor, ill-treated, long-suffering child." There is the same campaign to distort the children's loyalty, this time to turn them against their father. Some mothers-in-law are so aggressive in their tactics against their sons-in-law that they have earned themselves such epithets as "the old battle-axe." However, the battle-axe is not the most dangerous type of mother-in-law either for the son-in-law or the children. Children are not apt to be impressed by obviously belligerent behavior toward their father and may not only see through it, but resent it and align themselves with the forces of law and order.

Much more hazardous for both father and the children is the devious Machiavellian mother-in-law who moves quietly and efficiently and often talks in whispers.

Should the daughter show any signs of growing up under the tutelage of a fairly satisfactory marriage to a reasonable husband, occasionally, even offering the affront of mildly defending him, this experienced mom-in-law speedily moves up her verbal shock troops: "He won't be satisfied until you slave for him night and day." "You are losing your looks. You will be an old woman before your time." "I know men and their tricks." "Maybe you don't know it, but he wants you just for one thing." Various devices are used to keep the children in line and their vision at the level of immature emotional reactions.

Mom twirls her baton at the head of a long procession of surrogates. Should mom have to drop out of line, there are many competent to take her place—older children, bachelor uncles, and spinster aunts; cousins; occasionally a step-mother; old family friends. There are three surrogates, however, who deserve honorable mention—the governess, the nurse, and the school teacher.

There is a type of governess mentioned in awed whispers by some women as a "jewel." Undeniably she is competent. The children are always neat and clean; their manners are superb. When the family or the company do not want to be annoyed—well, as the mother remarks, "My children are scarcely a problem. Mademoiselle is perfect. She manages everything—and is so unobtrusive." There is the rub. Mademoiselle is too perfect; too unobtrusive. She is not quite so unobtrusive with the children. As it happens she is probably emotionally starved and love-parched. Life has never given her more than abortive opportunities of tapping the hidden but deep reservoirs of her emotional desires and yearnings. In the attempt to find compensations for that which she has never had, quietly, pathetically, but nonetheless dangerously for the future of the children, she stakes out large areas of their emotional lives and annexes the territory for herself. She is in a most intimate relationship with the children and can direct and control their thinking. *The children are her children.* Unfortunately, since she is their governess and not the wife of their father, she can only be a token mother. It is not sufficient to promote well-rounded maturing. By reason of her position in the household, Mademoiselle cannot be a mother. She must be a mom.

The emotional soil which the children should plant and tend and which this type of governess fences in and uses for herself sometimes cannot be reclaimed. I know a woman of 30, married and with two children, who only within the past year has been able to talk freely with her mother, or for that matter with any adult, particularly if in the family, or to listen to anything even remotely resembling advice. Inside herself, the figure of old "Nannie," her nurse and governess during childhood, would loom up and raise a silencing hand. Incidentally, this young woman still has a slight facial tic reminiscent of a tic which Nannie had.

There are trained nurses—spinsters, emotionally cheated by life. They do a perfect job of nursing children through a serious illness, tenderly, devotedly, and skillfully. Again there is the danger that they hold the children too closely; that when they finish the case and leave, they take something of the child with them that can never be replaced. I know a number of nurses who will nurse only children. The majority of them are emotionally mature women and do a fine piece of work professionally. A few equally skilled professionally are unsatisfied and immature emotionally. I fear that in their contacts with children the harm they do, owing to frustration in their own lives, outweighs the benefits of their technical nursing, no matter how expert it may be.

Children spend at least one half of their waking lives in direct and indirect contact with their school teachers. It is inevitable that in the vast army of school teachers there are many who, however intellectually able they may be and even though they may have graduated "cum laude" from a teachers' college, nevertheless are too immature emotionally to teach children. Much that children learn in schools is not to be found between the covers of school textbooks. The emotional lessons are even more important. The capacity to meet life squarely on an adequate give-and-take platform is rather more important than proficiency in algebra or a memory able to bound the States of the Union with celerity. Both intellectual information and emotional growth must reach a certain level in order to cope with the requirements of adult life. However, unless the intellectual measurements are notably insufficient, they can be added to from time to time, but cubits cannot be added suddenly to the emotional stature. Emotional additions must be not only in the correct quantity and of a specified quality but they must be placed in the structure of the personality at the proper time in the life of the child. Otherwise the personality structure will be top-heavy without sufficient underpinning, and it will not stand up against the adverse experiences of adult emotional and social life. It is literally true that every adult who has any considerable contact with children either adds something to or subtracts something from their maturing processes. Everything is recorded in the personality. Everything counts in the score of the future weal or woe of each child. School teachers are like other human beings. Some are mature; others immature. They cannot give children more than they have themselves. Their contact with children is very close and their opportunities of helping or harming are almost without limit.

As it happens the large number of school teachers are unmarried and many of them are no longer young. By no manner of means is the fact that the teacher is what used to be called an "old maid" necessarily any reason to fear that she will influence harmfully the emotional development of children. I know many teachers in this group who are fine, capable, and mature in their reactions to life. Their understanding and acceptance of their personal barricades of frustration have sweetened their characters and given them perspectives sometimes much more extended and mature than the vistas of those who have experienced the intimate emotional relationship of marriage.

To their great credit, these women have honor rolls of children they once taught in school—men and women who are doing important things or, at least, and this is even more to be acclaimed, men and women who are living their lives on a high plane of emotional and social maturity as mothers and wives, as fathers and husbands, as contributing citizens. These women teachers are strong allies to the mothers of the children. As for the children of moms the attitudes indoctrinated in the school environment often exert enough leavening influence to prevent them from becoming half-baked adults.

However, when a teacher, perhaps particularly a spinster, is a surrogate mom, she is one incarnate. She pours the vials of wrath of her own emotional disappointments and sufferings upon the children over whom she has authority—in full measure and overflowing. She may be an expert sadist capable of inflicting much more suffering than if she were permitted to use physical flagellation. She has available the instruments for the production of mental pain—rigid authority, unexplained punishment, "clever" sarcasm, power to humiliate the child before others. Of a poor boy who lived on "the other side of the tracks" and who was ten minutes late because he stopped to put out the ashes for his mother, such a teacher announced to her class, "I am afraid John's valet forgot to lay out his clothes this morning." It is as if these women said to the children, "I hate and resent you. I am going to make you suffer for the children I did not have. I will make it my business to prevent you from being happy mothers and fathers. Why should you have the things in life of which I was cheated?"

Strangely enough, such women generally have a pet or even several pets in the class. These youngsters are favored and their faults are readily condoned—they get away with anything. It would seem that even in these iron women there are a few vestiges of mothering which cannot be subjugated. Figuratively and sometimes literally the pets "pay through the nose" for the teacher's attention.

Then there is the teacher who is as lovable as her antithesis is detestable. She is loving and hopelessly sentimental toward the children. Nothing they do is wrong —"the little darlings." She cannot bring herself to discipline the children—"they are such babies." She has an endless repertoire of excuses for the shortcomings of "her" children and she dispenses these excuses lavishly to the other teachers, to the principal, and to the parents.

Neither of these types, the martinet or the sentimentalist, is helpful to mothers who are striving to assist their children to clear the high hurdles on the path to maturity. The hard teacher strews the path with the obstacles of stubbornness, a sense of injustice and resentment; the soft one makes the way so mushy that there is no solid ground for a "take-off." If the children have moms, there is a two-fold plot against the achievement of maturity— one in the schoolroom, the other in the home.

CHAPTER IX

MORE MOM SURROGATES

Not all substitute moms are flesh and blood. One surrogate can be found in sanatoriums, another in mental hospitals. One hides behind the cloak of religion. Another masquerades as an idea, behind which there may be a movement with momentum and power. Still another is disguised as a beneficent government. And, finally, there is the surrogate beginning beneficently and with maternal solicitude but ending with the ruthless domination of millions of human beings which finally destroys them.

It is significant how often in the childhood of psychoneurotic patients there is a well-marked pattern of immaturity, particularly in the mother. Often the pattern is exactly reproduced. A patient of mine had an hysterical paralysis of the right side of the body. Thirty years before, her mother who had always been immature and inadequate suffered a real "stroke," paralyzing the right side of her body.

Some time ago I sat with a Medical Board at a Philadelphia Naval Hospital. A young sailor was brought before the Board for disposition. Obviously he had been pitifully ineffective. His record was a consistent negative.

In the 18 months of his Navy service, there had been no positive behavior of any kind, not even transgressions against discipline. Three fourths of the time had been spent in hospitals. He had stomach symptoms—"funny feelings," "growlings," "gas," "turning," "belching," "sick stomach," "up-chucking (vomiting)," "misery." Exhaustive physical, laboratory, and X-ray studies failed to turn up any evidence of organic disease.

In disposition, the boy was described as good natured and he had never been known to lose his temper. However, sometimes when he was being teased by his fellow sailors, his face would suddenly get very red and he would compress his lips tightly together as though restraining an outburst of temper by main force. The patient readily explained this phenomenon: "Pappy and mammy told us kids brother Tom done gone out of his head, 'cause he done lose his temper. I aim to hole my temper I doan want to go crazy like brother Tom." Brother Tom was in the State Mental Hospital with schizophrenia.

The stomach symptoms were explained by a flash back into the home environment in which the patient lived until he was taken into the Navy. As long as he could remember his father had stomach "misery" and often "up-chucked" in front of the children. During his many years of stomach misery, "pappy" had accumulated a considerable store of gastrointestinal lore and reminiscences which he retailed to the children with much histrionic effect and to which they listened with spellbound attention. There were comparisons of innumerable diets, weird home remedies, strange twisting and writh-ing exercises, mysterious incantations at the full of the moon.

The patient was discharged from the service without a dissenting vote.

The psychoneuroses occupy very extensive territory in psychiatry and in life. On a scale drawn between fantasy and reality, between the average reactions of men and women in their daily lives and mental disease, the psycho-neuroses may be placed somewhat to the "left" of the reality line. They may be only a short distance to the left. Here are the men and women who have a few neurotic symptoms. Some such people compensate so adequately and in so many directions, that they are more competent and mature than many non-neurotics. I know a woman whose nineteen-year-old son is rendering splendid service in the Navy and whose two lovely daughters, seventeen and fifteen years old, daily demonstrate a fine maturity of thought and conduct. None of the children has ever suspected that for many years their mother has suffered considerable mental turmoil and apprehension whenever she is left alone. Many men in the armed forces made a good go of it and would not permit their neurotic symptoms to disbar them from serving their country. I know many pilots and other combat personnel who flew on dangerous missions carrying their psychoneurotic symptoms with them. Their symptoms did not decrease their deadly effectiveness against the enemy.

However, psychoneuroses are usually even more to the left of the reality marker, but still definitely nearer to it than to the unreality of mental disease. Only occasionally is a psychoneurosis close to this area. Nevertheless, the psychoneuroses are retreats from reality and the mental mechanisms by which emotional conflicts are transformed into neurotic symptoms are reality-evading techniques.

Psychoneurotic symptoms are many and varied. They may involve a massive loss of whole functions like walking, talking, seeing, or hearing. Or they may evidence themselves as headaches, backaches, tiredness, pains, aches, odd feelings here and there and everywhere, located in every organ and system—stomach and intestines, heart, lungs, genitourinary organs, skin. In other psychoneuroses, there are tensions, fear and chiefly anxiety—anxiety which has been cut loose from its original moorings so that the patient does not know what makes him so tense and anxious.

Adjacent to this clinical territory is an area in which the body and the emotions meet—an area in which an actual organic disease finally appears as the end result of long-continued and unsolved anxiety. For instance, it is now commonly accepted that an important factor in the production of peptic ulcer is long-enduring anxiety.

In another psychoneurosis, the patient is obsessed against his will by certain thoughts and is compelled either to do or not to do certain things. A gentleman in middle life, who enlisted in the British Army in World

War I and was discharged because of his psychoneurosis, was obsessed by the number "13" to such an extent that life became a burden. He *had* to stay in bed on the thirteenth day of the month and on the twenty-sixth. He *had* to count the words in the conversations of his friends, and at each thirteenth word, he experienced an unpleasant "shock." He *could not* walk in Piccadilly Circus in London because of a sign "Peter Robinson" advertising a department store. It contained 13 letters. And so on.

He was orphaned early in life by the death of both parents and was cared for by wealthy, elderly grandparents. Much of his care devolved upon an ignorant serving maid, who was grossly superstitious, particularly about the number "13." Seemingly, she was devoted to the boy. However, she was rather more than a mom for she seduced him sexually. The boy in his shame and anxiety repressed all conscious memory of what had happened and the first camouflaged evidence of it appeared some thirty years later when he became compulsive about the number "13."

I do not assert that all psychoneurotics had moms. However, I believe that very often they did. A psychoneurosis serves the same purpose mom served. The mom either by dominance or by soft subterfuge postponed the necessity of facing the hard and fast issues of adult emotional and social life and the making of decisions about them. By diverting attention to the contemplation of the symptoms, the psychoneurosis delays the facing and honest solution of the emotional conflict from which the neurotic symptoms were derived. It holds the patient in the protective bondage of his symptoms which make him feel important even though it be on a false and pathological basis. He is spared the belittling necessity of surveying his real insufficiencies and inadequacies. Decidedly, psychoneuroses may be mom surrogates, used by many who have not been able to achieve maturity.

There is a form of mental disease called schizophrenia or dementia praecox. In spite of the fact that under modern methods of treatment, more of these patients recover than formerly, schizophrenia still remains the psychosis which largely populates our mental hospitals. Psychiatry has only succeeded in parting slightly the veils which conceal the cause or causes of schizophrenia. Some day science will remove the veils altogether, and then we will know what produces this mental disease which annually removes many boys and girls from the world of the mentally alive and condemns them to dream away their lives in some hospital or asylum. Irrespective of whatever may be discovered, it will still remain true that schizophrenia in effect is a withdrawal from everyday life as we know it and live it.

The schizophrenic is the complete psychological isolationist. He can and frequently does "play dead," becoming a human 'possum, wrapped in a stupor in which he neither speaks nor moves and from which he cannot be aroused even by sharp needle thrusts. If the stupor is deep, the patient must be fed through a tube in order to maintain life. Psychiatrists of the psychoanalytical school have called attention to the curled-up position, the body compressed into the smallest space possible, in which these patients remain for long periods of time, sometimes for months or even years. They suggest it expresses an unconscious wish to return to the womb of the mother. However this may be, schizophrenia is a rejection of our world—a total acceptance of emotional and psychological defeat.

Many of these patients are defeated by life comparatively soon, often before the age of twenty. They are quickly vanquished. A few futile lances tilted with adult emotional and social responsibilities and they retire from the field.

Even before they step through the door of the psychosis, these children are more preoccupied and daydream more than other children. Even for the average child, the daydream rubs the lamp of fantasy. Its normal function is to reveal a world of compensation for the often irritating actual world, a land of satisfaction and happiness and of easy and wonderful conquest. In the children who are destined for schizophrenia, daydreaming is indulged in with increasing frequency and the return to the irksome everyday world becomes ever more difficult. Some youngsters succumb with but the feeblest protest; the behavior of others indicates a frantic struggle against being engulfed by unreality. Sooner or later, however, the door between the real and the make-believe, between actuality and fantasy, is closed and sealed.

The struggle is over. All is calm and at peace. The shadow of unreality has been transmuted into substance. In the paradise of fantasy, thinking is having. There is no bitter, grueling competition. Rewards and high places are gained without effort, without sweat, tears, and blood. These are the kings and queens of asylums. The unpleasant hard physical facts of life no longer exist, but its pleasures and satisfactions remain.

Schizophrenic women may have "children" by the "breath of the Holy Ghost" upon the pillows of their beds. Schizophrenia is an unfailingly kind and lavish mom.

Again, I am not suggesting that all youngsters who become schizophrenic had moms instead of mothers. It would not be true. I do believe, however, that an extremely large number did have moms, either maternal or paternal and sometimes both. I have practiced psychiatry too long and studied too many adolescent life histories to be deceived by momish tricks camouflaged as mother love. In many schizophrenic patients a true bill of indictment can be drawn against mom—indictment for failure to prepare the child to meet even the minimal demands of adult life. Sometimes the immaturity is so great and complete that the only path open for the child is the retreat into the fantasy—of schizophrenia—to remain there forever enwombed. There is little doubt that schizophrenia qualifies as a mom surrogate.

Perhaps the greatest boon of religion is in letting us feel dependent. When we are weak and frightened, we may find in God a tower of strength and support. Without loss of "face" or self-respect we can take to Him our mistakes and inadequacies, our humiliations and belittlements, our pitiful little subterfuges and hypocrisies, the injustices we have suffered and meted out to others. When we are hopelessly crushed by failure, God can remove the sting of defeat, soothe the hurt, and give us courage to try again.

To go to God in the right spirit is not weakening, but strengthening. No man is self-sufficient and strong enough to stand alone. The uncertainties and vicissitudes of life create an urgent need for normal dependency. Religion satisfies this need and if not misused gives the suppliant security. In the ideal God-man relationship there is a pattern which, even when it is imperfectly reproduced in the relationship between human beings, furnishes a basis for sound and enduring emotional and social maturity.

Religion, like everything else, cannot be only a matter of taking, never giving. In our daily lives there must be some effort to imitate the God-man relationship, however fumbling the effort may be. The chief return we can make to God for the strength and courage he renews in us is to try to help our fellow human beings. If we ask for everything and give nothing, we are weaving into our daily lives a pattern of selfish immaturity. It is almost as though we said to God, "I do not intend to meet even my ordinary obligations in life, but I am weak and You are strong. Therefore You will overlook my failings, continue to look after me and protect me from the consequences of what I do or do not do." In this way, religion may become an "opiate" for some people, who employ it to justify to themselves the ever-repeated and serious deficits in their relations with their fellow men. Then religion becomes a mom surrogate in which something fine is distorted from its noble purpose and made to mumble benedictions upon failure, inadequacy, and selfishness.

Moms should be interested in "movements" because often these become a refuge for the children they have left emotionally and socially stranded. This country seems to be the natural habitat of "movements." From "The Society for the Purification of the Body Politic" to "The Association for the Improvement of Dentistry for Small Animals" there is nothing too lofty or too lowly to escape the embraces of organization.

Many organized movements are excellent and constructive influences. Even should we disagree totally with their ideas and objectives, still intelligent minorities are a healthy leavening in our democracy. But too often movements are anything but helpful. The "idea" is not significant. It is only a dignified front for emotional sprees, diverting and intoxicating enough to permit the adherent to escape his adult responsibilities. The hallmark of such emotionalized movements, surrogates for mom, is the weakness of their grip upon reality and the child-minded personality they attract.

Intelligent and constructive movements may be identified by the amount of sound and accurate information that has been accumulated about the subject in which the members are interested and by what has been accomplished for the social good. The sincere worker in a worthwhile movement justifiably may identify himself with what has been done.

In the child-minded group, emotional weaknesses may be falsely fortified and spurious emotional strengths may be found by the merging of self with the cherished idea and, more significantly, with the idolized leader. Fostered by the intimacy which the group has with its leader and which he encourages, the identification and compensation are equivalent to those experienced by the small boy or girl, when he or she proudly announces, "My father is the smartest man in the world"; "My mother told me you should not do that." Such expressions are echoed by the immature movements enthusiast: "Good old Jim says we'll sweep the country. I shook hands with Jim once. Jim is smart." "They won't have so much to say after they read Bill's speech. I know Bill. I had a talk with him once."

A mob on the move for destruction and death is a bloody mom surrogate. The behavior of a mob plumbs noisome subterranean depths, and things come to the surface which cannot be seen at other times.

Something strange happens to the human being who participates in mob action. At some point, it appears that the unconscious mind which ordinarily directs so much of his everyday behavior is suspended and a kind of collective mob unconsciousness is in the saddle, riding herd roughshod. There is instantaneous and close identification with the mob leaders or leader. Whatever be the ethical code of each member of the mob, it is deeply breached and debased, and all inhibitions against destructive and murderous behavior are torn away. By merging himself with the leader, becoming as it were a part of him, the mobster escapes any feeling of personal culpability or responsibility for his conduct.

I am not suggesting even remotely that moms condition their sons to become members of bloodthirsty mobs. Of course they do not. It would be the last thing they would desire because of the danger involved. Nevertheless mobs are not recruited by chance. Only certain kinds of personalities are apt to be "caught out" in the wild torrent of a mob. Furthermore, mob candidates are likely to be men whose immaturity has relegated them to mediocre and obscure roles in life. The mob gives them the center of the stage, where they play a brief and bloody part. Unwittingly, moms contribute a considerable quota to mobs.

The resemblance between the ideology and philosophy of momism and national isolationism are more than accidental. The extreme isolationists tried to make us believe that it would be possible to fence in our country with a Chinese wall high enough to turn back any enemy attack by land, sea, or air. They assured us that we would be completely invulnerable to military invasion. I have not heard this assurance for some time, since in view of recent developments it is conceivable that the next war might last but a few minutes, perhaps being decided by a single robot plane, its flight directed by television, put down on its objective by radar, and carrying a load of annihilation in the shape of atomic bombs. We were assured, too, that the isolationist wall could not be breached by economic, political, or ideological spearheads of penetration. We were to retire behind this wall and live happily ever after.

The isolationists hoped to sell the idea to the nation by two-fold propaganda: 1. The security we would experience if we adopted the plan; 2. The dire dangers to which we would be exposed if we did not adopt it.

Much of the same bi-faceted technique is employed by moms. Here the emphasis is on the peace and happiness of the home and the danger of entangling alliances. The theme song is "There's no place like home," played with innumerable variations—"After all, there *is* no place like home," "I have never seen a home just like this." In this last there is implied warning, particularly to a son, "You won't ever find a home just like this. You had better think twice before you leave it."

The cement that binds the happy little home together is invisible but very cohesive. In the last analysis, mom's isolationism has a much better chance of surviving than has political isolationism. The protecting wall which the political isolationists proposed erecting was too concrete. The proof of its vulnerability was too readily demonstrable. The description of the first robot bomb was sufficient to cause widespread desertion from an already waning cause.

The Army is so structured that it could become a mom surrogate. Necessarily there must be regimentation and discipline. Soldiers must be told what to do and what not to do, and there is not the time or place for explanatory detail. In return for military duty and obedience, the soldier receives protection, not only in the field when the going is "rough," or when he is sick or wounded, but also in camps where he is fed and sheltered. The soldier is instructed in the techniques of combat; he is conditioned for battle through lessons in self-protection against sickness, wounds, and death. Amusements and diversions are furnished. There is a large amount of routine, and ordinarily the soldier makes relatively few decisions. In a good army, there is a close dependence-relationship between soldiers and their officers. The right kind of an officer feels responsible for his men and in some sense regards them affectionately and protectingly as his children. Soldiers not only like and respect a capable, conscientious officer, but they look to him for help, protection and counsel, when they are in a "jam" not necessarily with respect to the Army but about all kinds of difficulties including home problems. The stage would seem to be set for "child-soldier" "mom-officer" relationships, dangerously promoting immaturity.

From my military experiences I am convinced that the danger of making youngsters overdependent has not been either widespread or serious. In the speedy preparation for this war a great many civilians suddenly, much too abruptly, had to be made into officers. Even though usually they were technically qualified and well-trained, many of them lacked qualities of leadership. But, whatever their shortcomings, they were not likely to produce or greatly increase immaturity in the men in their command.

Many officers, but not nearly enough, were born leaders of men and dealt with the soldiers they led on a mature level. They added appreciably to the development of many youngsters and often completed the emotional and social maturing processes begun by their mothers. Wisely they checked retreats into childish and sometimes dangerously immature behavior. On one of my military missions I met a captain of artillery who was packing his kit, his division having been alerted for overseas. He told me of an experience he had with one of his men several months before and asked my psychiatric judgment upon the way he had handled it.

One evening, Pfc. Smith, 21 years old and married

three months, came to him in a state of terrific turmoil. In his hand, which was trembling with emotion, he held a letter from his wife, telling him she was pregnant by a man whom she loved. She stated plainly enough that she wished just one thing from Smith—a divorce. Smith was a two-fisted fellow. "Sir," he said, "I'm going back to tell off that two-timing bitch and maybe kill that bastard. Would the captain get me a few days' leave?" The captain replied, "I could get you the leave, I guess, but I wonder if it would be such a good idea. Of course, if I don't get it for you, you could 'go over the fence.' But how about this? I'll give you a pass to go to town tonight. I know you could clear out, but I don't believe you will. You're too good a soldier. I'm counting on you to help me with the new men who are still pretty green. And, Smith, I hope you don't mind my 'butting in,' but I'm sorry that you got such a rotten deal. Maybe it can be fixed. If you feel like it come in to see me in the morning. I'll be looking for you."

Smith took his pass and went into town. He took a few drinks, a very few in view of the situation. He saw the captain the next morning. It was Smith and not the captain who decided the wife was a "no good." The thing to do was to write and tell her to get a divorce.

The captain concluded by saying, "Sergeant Smith has been fine ever since. I'm sure counting on him for D-Day. I know he will turn in a good job."

I said, "I thought you said he was a private."

"Oh, he was but he was made corporal the day after he got the letter from his wife and sergeant three weeks ago."

I told the captain I didn't think he needed any psychiatric guidance.

The sons of mothers are not likely to be turned back on the path of maturity by military life. They were willing to serve and do a good job but their attitude was apt to be, "Let's get it over with as soon as we can. I want to get home where I belong."

Even though freed of responsibility and the need of making decisions, mom's boys did not want to stay in the Army either. It wasn't soft enough. There was too much unpleasant and sordid duty; not enough consideration and too much danger.

There was a considerable group of over-age officers for whom the Army was a satisfactory mom. I am not referring to the many officers who had special capacities and skills much needed in the war emergency. Usually they were mature men who sacrificed money, position, their home lives and civilian ways of living to which they were accustomed and which they liked, because they felt it was their duty to serve. Their records speak for them.

I do mean some of the "old boys" who just had to "sacrifice everything and go at once." Often the sacrifice meant exchanging the responsibilities and problems of marital life for a desk job in Washington. Although they complained bitterly of the arduous duty and the crowded condition of the Washington trains, they really enjoyed it hugely, uniform and all, perhaps particularly the uniform. Life as an Army bachelor need not be too unpleasant. There were compensations. For one thing, home and its problems were pleasantly remote. A man busy serving his country scarcely can be expected to help work them out.

CHAPTER X

MOM IN A BOTTLE

One of the most dangerous of the mom surrogates comes in a bottle. The surrogate I refer to is alcohol, and to the alcoholic it is indeed a substitute for mom. To the heavy drinker, it provides all the protection, all the escape from life's hard knocks, and all the synthetic feeling of well-being that mom provides.

The alcohol addict—and alcoholism is an addiction—generally turns to alcohol for one main, underlying reason—*he is immature*. Basically, he lacks the adult ability to face the problems of life. Alcohol gives him a pleasant, easy escape from reality. In about 80 percent of the alcoholic cases I have studied, momism in childhood was the basic, underlying cause. Again, the man or the woman was left out on an emotional limb by a mom who protected her children in their youth and would not let them grow up. These were the children who were told what to do and when to do it. They were allowed to make few decisions of their own. In the end, they were left totally unprepared to meet even the minimal standards of intelligent grown-up living. They never matured.

Let me state a typical case history:

John H's "mother" was over forty when he was born and, since he was the only child, and probably would be the only child, she became determined to keep and protect him at all costs. From his earliest days he was coddled and pampered. She fought his battles for him; made his decisions for him; would not let him take an active part in sports; picked out his friends, his clothes, and even the books he read. In short, she dominated him completely.

From the time John was old enough to walk and talk he was shy and timid. He wanted to be accepted as "one of the boys," but his desires to conform in such things as dress, play, and general activities in and out of school were completely and thoroughly thwarted by mom. As a result, he was picked on and bullied. He was called a sissy and a mamma's boy. He was teased and laughed at. Naturally his shyness increased. He fast developed all the traits and behaviors of an introvert in spite of the fact that he wanted to be otherwise.

The story was no different when he entered an eastern university. He did find acceptance within a certain group, but they were very much like himself. Then, during his junior year, he made a discovery—after a few drinks he found that his shyness seemed to fade. After a few more drinks he felt he could meet people, talk, and enter into things. He embraced alcohol as a new-found friend and protector—it solved his problems for him, it dulled the sharp edge on the knife of reality, it provided a protective shell that mom no longer could give him.

He didn't realize it then, but by the time John graduated from college he was well on his way to alcoholism. It usually takes about five years from the time a person realizes his continued need for alcohol before he begins to feel that alcohol is as important as food and sleep. In most cases, he finally slips completely into the realm of unreality and fantasy and must have alcohol to keep him there. By dulling his senses, it provides an easy way to escape the problems and the unpleasant things of life. Everything seems easier. The alcoholic, like the schizophrenic, lives in a world of his own making.

John H. is forty now and completely cured of his addiction by psychological re-education. However, one mom trait persists—he still feels shy and self-conscious in spite of the fact that he now is a very successful professional man.

Most times—eight times out of ten—the childhood pattern of the alcoholic is pretty much the same. Emotional immaturity is the seed, introversion is the soil, and alcoholism is the final growth. In their desire to escape reality and throw off responsibilities, some of mom's children discover the magic of the bottle. They find in it an escape that is easily obtainable and not socially reprehensible. Alcohol makes them feel good. More than that, it makes them feel strong and self-reliant. Later on it produces agreeable fantasies. The world is no longer disagreeable and unkind. Viewed through their whisky glasses, it is rosily pleasant. It seems even better than having mom to look after them and protect them. Alcohol is a mom that can be poured into a glass.

I have often been asked, "What is the difference between a normal drinker and an abnormal drinker?" The normal drinker is one who drinks socially to make the moment more pleasurable and companionable. The abnormal drinker is one who drinks to escape reality. Usually he cannot, or will not, face life—taking the sorrows with the joys and the bad with the good. He unconsciously wants life to be a continuation of his sheltered childhood and alcohol provides him with the pleasant unreality and make-believe that he desires. Usually he begins by using alcohol as a boost to help him over the rough spots, but soon it becomes more important than the boost it gives.

Many times the alcoholic will blame his addiction on his marriage, his business, or his "health." Again, a psychiatrist digging into the background of the case usually will find immaturity based on the inevitable mom.

Not long ago a wealthy and successful business man came to me with a family problem. He was thirty-four and his brother, Walter, two years younger, had become completely addicted to alcohol; so much so that after a week of drinking he would come home and abuse his wife, usually climaxing his drunken tirade by holding her out the window with threats to drop her.

The case history of the family showed the familiar pattern of a mom. The eldest son, the one who had come to me, and a younger daughter had been strong enough to assert themselves and escape the silver cord, but the brother Walter had become completely and hopelessly enmeshed. Being a well-to-do family, the mom had used wealth—roadsters, long trips, big allowances—as the reward for doing her bidding. She had carried her "gold" silver cord to such a point that she cut the daughter out of her will completely when the girl showed signs of growing away.

Walter followed the familiar pattern to the line. When his mom died he tried unsuccessfully to substitute his sister. When that failed, he started drinking heavily. Then, again strictly according to pattern, he married an immature wife. The marriage naturally was a poor union from the start, in spite of the fact that several children were born.

Walter's wife has since died, and thanks to mature handling on the part of the brother and sister and most of all by his wife's sister, who moved in to take care of the children, Walter for the first time in his life is showing signs of wanting to grow up. His battle is far from won, but so far the sister-in-law is doing a fine job. At last, he is beginning to make his own decisions.

Since the important factor in the production of alcoholism is childhood-determined immaturity and indecision, the logical treatment is psychological re-education to produce more maturity and decision. To his surprise and inner dissatisfaction, the patient discovers that the wise physician declines to be a mom. He does not tell him what to do and what not to do. From the very beginning the physician refuses to deal with anything but the mature segment of the alcohol addict's personality, however small it may happen to be. The patient must make his own decisions and, once he starts, he begins to grow up. The patient himself must decide, "Shall I serve cocktails to friends?" "Shall I keep liquor in the house?" "Should I go to the corner bar with the boys?"

Once the mother or mature wife understands what the doctor is trying to accomplish for the alcoholic son or husband and appreciates the sound reasons for his technique, she becomes a helpful ally. Not so with mom. Never is she more than halfway convinced and she is likely to follow her own system. She is among the patient watchers at the front door, awaiting the abnormal drinker's return. She is of the expert sniffers of breaths, seemingly able to detect alcohol in quantities smaller than can be discovered by the police. She rewards periods of abstinence by affectionate displays and often by lavish material gifts; she punishes alcoholic indulgences by withdrawing rewards. The alcohol addict is treated as a child. The momish wife has advantages over the mom. I have known several wives who doled out sexual intercourse in exchange for so many days or weeks of abstinence from alcohol. Of course, the continuance in the home of such immaturity-prolonging conditions nullifies the doctor's efforts. He cannot compete with mom.

CHAPTER XI

HOMOSEXUALITY

Many cases of homosexuality are, of course, deeply rooted in biological deviations. However, there are many instances in which it seems reasonable to implicate an immaturity determined by mom and her wiles. In some sense then, these cases of homosexuality may be viewed as mom surrogates.

Since it is universal that every male child, at least at first, is in love with his mother, it naturally follows that a very large portion of sex development and progress toward heterosexuality is determined by the attitude of the mother. What serious harm may be done by wrong momish attitudes is illustrated by quotations from a letter which I recently received. In all my years as a practicing psychiatrist, this is one of the most pathetic letters of its kind that I have ever seen:

"Dear Professor Strecker,

"I have just read 'Are American Moms a Menace?' in the *Ladies Home Journal*. I am a sixteen-year-old boy; a 'sissy,' a 'mother's boy.'

"I am ashamed to take my problem to my parents or to a doctor whom I would have to *see*, so I am writing to you. Please try to understand and help me. I guess I am a homosexual. (It hurts deeply to say, think, or write that word. Even to *hear* it!). I do not care at all for girls except from an artist's view. You see, my hobby is make-up and fashion designing. I scrutinize every woman's make-up and grooming, but have no desires sexually. I don't even date. But I have to keep myself from staring at a handsome boy or man. This is awful! I am not dumb; my teachers say I am actually bright but I am lazy.

"My father is so narrow-minded and mean and old-fashioned, while my mother and I are broad-minded and modern. I adore my mother, though it's not half her fault. I insist on kissing and hugging her, though it 'gets on her nerves.' Frequently I can't talk to my father he is so repulsive.

"The only sexual satisfaction I get is masturbation and an occasional 'offer.' How disgraceful! I'd sooner die than let mother know. My mother is what I suppose you would call 'frigid.' She said she dreaded the thought of sexual relations and was engaged seven times before she married Daddy (she was very beautiful and popular, though). Could this have anything to do with my troubles?

"I've often thought of being someone's wife. You see, all my life my viewpoints have been as if I were a woman, and I almost am. Till I was thirteen I dressed in women's clothes often, but just for a few minutes in private, of course. Still I make myself up (in private also).

"Please, Dr. Strecker, try to understand and analyze my case. I beg of you.

"Please forgive the hasty and inefficient way in which

I have written this letter. I had to write fast so I could remember all I wanted to say and before I lost my nerve.

"Many, many thanks, and write very soon!

"Sincerely,

"XXXXX"

A few parts of the original letter have been eliminated in the interests of good taste and because they added little to the case. The essential parts are there, and unedited, and a study of them shows two familiar types of silver cords—"you will never find anyone quite as pretty and worthy of you as mom," and "sexual intercourse is a horrible affair in which the husband is the beast." Mom, as the boy paints her in his letter, is undoubtedly the "pretty addlepate" who by her actions and what she has said and implied has poisoned the boy's mind against normal, mature heterosexual living. In various ways, probably mostly devious, he has been made to know that no girl ever could measure up to his mom, so he veered away from the normal companionship with girls that are a part of every normal high school boy's life. Sex was degrading, unnatural, undesirable—his mom had told him so. Naturally, when completely entwined by these two silver cords, his normal, healthy masculine instincts were stifled. The result—a tendency toward abnormal sex life.

In some cases, I have known another silver cord to be the cause. Here the mom wants a girl and a boy is born. Not to be done out of her wish, she raises the boy more like a daughter than a son—she dresses him in frilly, fancy clothes; keeps his hair long for several years beyond the normal time; takes him with her wherever she goes; makes him play with girls instead of boys; in short, deliberately makes him feminine. I know of one case where the mom dressed her son in girl's clothing, with accompanying long hair, until he was ten. What could do more to give a child a warped unreal idea of sex? How can such a child ever hope to live a normal heterosexual life?

A mom who gets too much personal satisfaction from her son's deep attachment to her as his "love object" and prefers to continue as his "light of love," instead of freeing him gently but firmly and guiding him along the path of normal sexual development which ends in mature heterosexuality, often sows the seeds of latent or even overt homosexuality in her son. Subconsciously the boy has "fallen in love" with his mother, but feels a sense of guilt at even unconsciously thinking of his mother sexually. Unless the mother cuts the silver cord and allows him to mature, free of her, this sense of guilt is transferred from then on to the various mother surrogates—girls and women—in his later life. Thus heterosexuality in a complete way is impossible for him to achieve and he may turn to homosexuality in his need for some sex outlet, as the lesser evil.

All these same forces operate against the daughters of immature fathers—pops—as well as against the sons of moms. The pop who mentally seduces his daughter may implant a tendency toward lesbianism.

I have had a young man say to me, "Doctor, I have all of the normal sex instincts. My reactions when I see a beautiful girl or woman in a tight-fitting sweater or a revealing bathing suit are the same as any normal man's, but then I stop and think: what would my mom say if I thought such thoughts about her." His main desire is not to harm his mother-image.

I want to repeat that while innate factors often go into the making of homosexuality, yet the environmental influence is strong enough so that moms and pops are to blame.

CHAPTER XII

"MOMARCHIES"

Naziism *was* (hopefully I am using the past tense) a mom surrogate with a swastika for a heart. At first there was a semblance of a heart. In fact, there was a reasonable facsimile of one. The Germans were made unhappy, humiliated, and frustrated by the defeat sustained in World War I. The majority of Germans were deprived, many of them seriously deprived, particularly in the matter of food, and the Germans like good food and plenty of it.

True enough, the sad situation of *der kleiner mann,* the little fellow, was largely his own fault. Eagerly and enthusiastically he had obeyed the command to wage World War I—a command given by the mom of twenty-five years before, the Emperor and the General Staff. True, too, was it that for a long time the large proportion of German citizens had lived under the domination of the Army General Staff, mom and her handmaidens, the Prussian officer caste. Not only did they live under it, but they rather liked it. At least, they cheered vociferously at the goose-stepping and the fine, brave panoply of war.

After World War I, composite Hans Schmidt was sad, rather hungry and, all in all, quite miserable. Then an opportunist appeared on the national horizon. Perhaps he was a demagogue. Probably he was something much more dangerous than a demagogue—a sincere blood-letting fanatic, either insane or very close to it. The Fuehrer had all the qualities and ingredients which go into the making of a super-mom. He even had the feminine note of hysteria which may be heard in the voices of moms when they are battling for their children and, if need be, are willing to give their lives for them.

So this hysterical voice screamed its message throughout the length and breadth of Germany, a message of love and devotion for his children; a promise that he would cherish and protect them and deliver them from bondage. And because of many things and circumstances, including the uncertainty and vacillating policies of democratic nations and the gullibility of an old man with an umbrella, Mom Schickelgruber was able to fulfill many of his promises. The lot of the common man was improved. There were thousands upon thousands of his brothers and sisters, whom the Fuehrer indignantly said had been abducted from the German family. He would bring these abused children back to the family fold. He *did*. Furthermore, he assuaged their wounds and restored their pride. Here indeed was a mom who never forgot his children. Incidentally, he never permitted the children to forget him.

The Fuehrer did much more. The German "children" felt inferior and belittled. The other children would not play with them; mocked and derided them. These other children had all the food and all the nice things in life. They had even "stolen" the iron from which shining guns and other war pretties could be made. "Don't fret, children, Mom Fuehrer will fix it. He knows his children have been grossly discriminated against. He knows the others hate and abuse you, have stolen what belongs to you, and are plotting to destroy you. Mom won't permit that." So he marched in and *took back the iron*.

These were only trifles. "There are much greater things in store for my children." Not only would he teach their enemies to respect them, but he would lay them prostrate at their feet. Did not the children realize they were not ordinary children? They were super-children, super-men racially. They were of the *Herrenvolk* destined to rule the world. No longer abject little Hans Schmidt, but Grossherr Johann Schmidt, World Conqueror and Ruler. He would bring them slaves to work for them. The children could humiliate and torment them, thus demonstrating and practicing their superiority. *He did and they did.*

The children must remember that the obligation of children, particularly German children, is unfailing obedience and unfailing love for their mom. Of course, they would want to obey the commands of the mom who loved them so much, gave them so much, and did everything for them. Among other things, they must have nothing to do with those others, who hated them and had been so unkind to them. They must not even listen to them over the radio. Their lying voices would sully the family circle and might even breed dissension and discontent.

Now the heart began to fade out and the stark and cruel outlines of the swastika emerged. Every moment of time, every act of daily living, and even every thought were prescribed. Mom would not tolerate disobedience. Those who disobeyed were punished by being shut in the closet—the closets of the concentration camps. Mom wielded a bloody whip of torture and death.

Finally the hold over the children became so absolute it was no longer necessary to court their favor. They were safely enwombed. It was even possible cynically to disregard their feelings and give them a book by mom in which they could read plainly enough that the masses must be controlled and their thinking directed and that the bigger the lie the more likely it would be believed.

By and large, talent for self-government does not rank high among the many German skills and abilities. In the matter of governing themselves wisely, there is an appalling social immaturity. This immaturity has been bred into the bone during childhood under the tutelage of the military caste. It is not at all surprising that the first roll of the thunder, threatening a storm, and the first drops of the rain of adversity should send the German people scurrying back to the mom from whom they have never been far away; to hide under her apron, to be comforted and told what to do. With one exception,

Germany has been the most complete "momarchy" of all times.

Japanese psychology, on the other hand, is strangely compounded of a racial sense of inferiority strongly over-compensated, modern efficiency more imitative than original, and the mysterious fatalism of the East. It is quite alien to Western mores and cultures.

Nipponese momism was more personalized than the Nazi brand. Figuratively, the august presence of the lineal descendant of the sun god, the Emperor, was the reposi-tory of the eternal womb to which all loyal Japanese hoped to return. During the war, this pious hope was heartily seconded by our fighting men who did all they could to bring about its speedy realization.

The Emperor was, and I'm afraid still is by most Japanese, revered as a god. Just before the last days of the war, in order to encourage his children whose fac-tories and homes had been gutted by American fire-bombs, he condescended to permit his likeness to be re-produced in the daily press. An educated and cultured Japanese trembled with awe as with veiled gaze he looked at the picture of his Emperor. Even though he knew how dark the war outlook was, at once he felt abso-lutely convinced of ultimate victory. Some years before the war an American magazine published a picture of the Emperor. There was a politely worded request from Japan to the American public that the issue containing the Emperor's picture be handled carefully, that it not be held upside down, and above all, that no other article be placed upon it.

Fortunately for us, Japanese momism worked too well. The desire to be enwombed was too strong. Often it led to unnecessary and wasteful loss of Nip manpower. The Japanese soldier knew little of mass defense. Consequently when situations became tight, there were apt to be a series of wildly enthusiastic banzai charges which were not only one-way tickets to death but were militarily futile. While the "divine" spirit of the Emperor pervades the battlefields, he cannot of course be on hand in his physical presence. The officer is the surrogate for the Emperor. He may be overanxious to greet his honorable ancestors. An officer with seven remaining soldiers encountered about the same number of marines. There was an even chance of fighting it out. The officer ordered his men to kneel around him in a circle. Expertly he decapitated them and then did a faultless job of hara-kiri on himself. But ordinarily, if trapped, the Nip soldier fought like a cornered rat, though as an individual he thought far less quickly and was far less resourceful than the average American soldier. This is the logical penalty that must be paid for national momism.

Nipponese fatalistic bravery was constructed of the observance of a rigid military code, strengthened by propaganda-induced fear of what would be done to prisoners and animated by a mystic national religion. It was armed with a Samurai sword and bedecked in a ceremonial robe, concealing the most gigantic and cruelest mom fraud ever perpetrated upon millions of socially immature human beings.

I doubt if even the atomic bomb had sufficient explosive force to dis-womb the Japanese people. After Japan yielded, thousands of Japanese bowed to the ground before the walls of the palace, abjectly begging the Emperor-Mom to forgive them for not having tried harder to win the war!

CHAPTER XIII

MOM AND THE VETERAN

Demobilization is a big word. It means far more than taking apart an Army and a Navy—the business of bringing the boys home from foreign ports and speeding them through separation centers. It means successfully re-absorbing them into normal civilian life; re-orienting them personally, occupationally, and socially.

Unfortunately some people and some organizations feel that every veteran must be an emotional and social problem. Even if a veteran thinks he is not a problem, they are willing and eager to convince him and his family that he is. He simply *must* be a problem.

Some of us are better equipped than others to help the veteran. One wife writes me she is fearful that her husband, who was "kind and considerate" before he went to war, will be brutal and cruel to the children because he has killed so many Japs. Another is worried because her husband wrote from overseas that he attended divine services every Sunday: "Do you think he will want to continue after he gets home? He never went to church before." A Navy wife's husband wrote to her every day from the Pacific. She was worried. "Do you think he will be disappointed if I don't keep the letters? I have a very small apartment." No matter how adequately we prepare to receive and readjust the veteran, I predict that the measure of our success or failure will be the maturity of the veteran himself—or his lack of it—and our own maturity.

Military life—with its subordination of individual desires for the good of the whole, its strict regimentation, its risks, discomforts, and loneliness, and its fears—is a strain. At the end of a war, a soldier is supposed to go back immediately to his old ways of life. He is supposed to change his habits and his emotions almost overnight. Even normal healthy unwounded men are bound to show marked reactions to these sudden demands and changes. The reactions will vary from indifference, depression, fear, lack of confidence, and a feeling of failure to impatience, restlessness, extreme irritability, and belligerency. Don't blame the veteran, the reactions are normal. Time must be allowed for the readjustment. The armed services took months to train their men and condition them mentally, physically, and emotionally. Isn't it reasonable to expect that re-orientation will take as long or longer? The entire burden of readjustment must not be placed entirely on the veteran's shoulders. It is a cooperative matter of give-and-take between the veteran and those around him—*maturity* is necessary on both sides.

There are at least four factors governing the readjustment of the veteran to civilian life. Two of them are variables and somewhat unpredictable.

The first factor is the man as he was before he entered

the service, with all his assets and liabilities, the man in his total personality. The second factor is a variable. It is the change wrought in the soldier by his war experiences. No one can live through a war, particularly in combat areas, without having something happen to his personality. That something is not predictable. I have talked with many men who have killed the enemy, sometimes in gruesome, bestial, primitive hand-to-hand struggles. Some of these men were loud, aggressive and tough in civilian life. Others were quiet and reflective, likely to regret their battle performance. Still others took the experience in their stride. They had not enjoyed the killing except perhaps in the brief, blood-red moment of battle. Now that it is in the past they shrug their shoulders, "It was my job," or "It was my life or his." In a fighting war, men die a thousand deaths but live a thousand new lives.

Many men fought and lived successfully in environments to which they were neither physiologically nor psychologically suited—far beneath the surface of the sea or in the substratosphere where they would have died of air hunger if they had not been fed oxygen through tubes. One may be reasonably sure that a submarine will submerge, but there is no guarantee that it will rise to the surface again. The plane will go up, but whether it will come down to earth intact with a living crew, or drop, a flaming, twisted mass of wreckage, its crew dead, cannot be forecast.

Some of these men from the ocean's depths and from the

sky's heights will walk awkwardly at first on city streets. They will need help. After all, it is not easy to come up through the fathoms of the sea, where, with a simple movement of his wrist, one could send destruction and death streaking toward an enemy ship, or be translated from a level of 40,000 feet where the airman was omnipotent and could drop death with a push of a button, to a humble humdrum clerkship in a large office, with home a tiny crowded suburban house, and the social event of the week a movie or an evening of bridge.

The third factor is the home situation as it was before the man departed for the war. All that may be said of it is that it will not be the same as it was when the soldier left.

The last factor is the home situation to which the veteran returns. The mere passage of time has brought change. Often the changes are breath-taking. There may be a wife whom he scarcely knows. Before he left there was only time for a few weeks of romantic honeymooning, and then a hiatus of one, two, three, or more years. The veteran may even have to sort out the names of strange in-laws. There may be a child he has never seen. His wife may be a busy worker in an office or a factory, not too enthusiastic about relinquishing her job and returning to dependent domesticity.

Of one thing we may be sure. No matter how mature he was, each man has passed through a period of excitement, of restlessness, and boredom. He has experienced some degree of disillusionment. In the war, wherever he fought it, the one bright, sustaining thought was HOME. At those cheerless times of hardship and deprivation, it was natural enough that home should be overidealized. Things were put in it that were never there. Things were expected of it that could never materialize.

Now the soldier is home from the wars. There is a brief passing moment of welcome, of home-coming and great joy, never to be forgotten. From then on realization does not quite come up to anticipation. Little clouds appear on the horizon. The old home town is not quite "what she used to be." The "gang" is gone, some to distant parts of the country, others still remain in the Army. The girl, or the wife, is happy to have him back, but she has made various occupational and social commitments. She likes her job, has made new friends and cannot be expected to drop them at once. Or the housekeeping seems a little slipshod. Perhaps, "it wouldn't be such a bad idea to follow a system like we had in the Army." The returning veteran feels perhaps that his wife has gained entirely too much independence during his absence. The family, who at first hung breathlessly upon every word of his adventures and exploits, begin to get a little bored, hiding it politely behind smothered yawns. The veteran begins to miss the old outfit, wondering where they are and what they are doing—"they were good guys, interested in a fellow."

The veteran finds the restrictions of civilian life irksome, only he does not use the word "irksome." His description is stronger. The scarcity of consumer goods, the crowded restaurants, the shortage of housing, the spectacle of waste and lavish spending all bother him. At the end of the first week, even the most sensible veteran is apt to declare, at least under his breath, "Hell of a way to treat a veteran."

By and by the veteran gets a job—regular hours and a time clock to punch. Army life with all its shortcomings and dangers was comparatively free-and-easy, even in the forward areas. This is different. His fellow employees, who had not been in service, are treated as well as he, "maybe a little better." The boss is "a cranky old guy," who doesn't know much about handling men. The veteran's former captain could have told the old boy a few things. Probably the veteran goes through a short phase of railing and sarcasm directed at defense workers and "4-F's."

All this and much more is quite within normal limits, temporarily. Reasonably soon the mature sons of mothers find themselves. The situation begins to get easier and better. They gain increasing adjustment, security, and happiness in their personal, vocational, and social lives.

Generally, it will not be so with the sons of moms. Mom's grasping hand and silver cord will reach out and gather together her own. She will see to it that they do not forget the sacrifices they have made, the discriminations against them, the debt the nation owes them. No doubt some of these men, many years from now when they are old and decrepit, will be carrying signboards "Unfair to Veterans."

The GI Bill of Rights extends many benefits, privileges, and opportunities to veterans. Not too many—perhaps not enough for those who were wounded in body or in mind, for *all who served well*. It would be unfortunate if those who gave so much should be crowded out by the "takers" who gave little or nothing. There is one benefit, however, they will not be able to collect, the boon of emotional and social security. Mom and her surrogates by never freeing them and by firmly re-tying the apron strings as soon as they returned have barred them from that benefit—forever.

CHAPTER XIV

SO SHALL WE REAP

The effect of mom and her activities goes far beyond the single individual or individuals that she dominates in childhood. Her effect is cumulative and far-reaching. William Ross Wallace put down no idle words when he wrote, "The hand that rocks the cradle is the hand that rules the world."

At the moment, the social portrait of man is very incomplete. Were it even half finished, the world would have scarcely embroiled itself in two bloody and destructive wars in the short space of twenty-five years. Many eons must elapse and many additions and subtractions must be made to the portrait before man will merit the simple designation homo sapiens.

Each individual unit, each man and each woman, you and I, may be symbolized by a circle. The circle, when it is complete, is the ideal—a human being in even contact with his environment. Each circle, representing one person, is surrounded by a series of concentric circles. The circles immediate to the personal circle signify the human being's personal rights—a *very few* sacred personal rights such as the right to protect and preserve his life, the right to bar unwanted intruders from his home, the right to worship God as his conscience dictates, the right to think independently though not always to carry his thoughts into action. There are a few really personal rights, but not many.

Beyond the limited group of circles of personal liberties, there are many more circles. They represent the rights we share with others. These circles overlap similar circles surrounding other individuals and are mutually held territory. Highly placed, or lowly placed, no one has more than a fractional claim upon this jointly occupied area. It is in this "give-and-take" land—the overlapping of rights and responsibilities—that the fate of democracy will be decided.

The capacity to live democratically and constructively is acquired only in childhood. Only reasonably mature parents, and particularly mature *mothers,* are competent to teach their children these lessons of democracy by permitting them to perfect their social instincts in their relations with other children. If the intermediate territory of "give-and-take" is populated with the sons and daughters of moms and their surrogates, then democracy cannot stand. It has happened elsewhere; it can happen here.

Even our highly prized and unwillingly relinquished personal rights sometimes must be modified, inhibited, and even yielded to others. Democracy means just that. Self-preservation is a dominant natural law, yet it must be tempered where others are concerned. If in war, during an enemy raid, there are no unoccupied fox holes, a soldier must not forcibly eject another soldier from a shelter and take his place. A sailor blasted into the sea from his ship by the enemy torpedo has no right to tear another sailor away from a life raft, in order to take his place.

And so it is with civilian living as well. We cannot advance ourselves at the expense of others, even if it is a case of "you *or* me."

Many years ago a friend of mine told me of a church service he once attended in a small New England town. The minister was the typical old-church clergyman. The subject of his sermon was "Brotherly Love," and during the course of it he told of visiting another minister who was scheduled to deliver a Sunday morning sermon at a small church in a very small rural community. When he and his eight-year-old son, who made the trip with him, arrived about an hour before service time, the first thing they saw as they entered the church was a large box labelled "Contributions." The visiting minister reached into his pocket, pulled out a fifty-cent piece, and dropped it into the box.

After the services, one of the elders of the small church congratulated the minister on behalf of the congregation and said, "It is our custom to pay the visiting minister half of the contributions that have been made." When the box was opened, it contained one coin—a half dollar— whereupon the young son spoke up, "Daddy, if you had put more in you would have got more out."

Putting, not getting, is the basis of a happy, mature life and a true democracy. Moms, by not allowing their children to grow up under the give-and-take rules of existence, not only spoil life for their sons and daughters, but threaten the very foundation upon which our democracy is built, for the pattern laid down in childhood is followed throughout our lives.

When it is a question of privileges and favors to be obtained I suspect that the children of moms are in the majority in the forum of public opinion, with both arms extended. When it is a matter of obligations to be fulfilled, or unpleasant duty to be done, they are likely to be found gazing intently out of the window.

The laws governing cause and effect are inexorable. The very existence of the physical sciences depends on the fact that when a known cause is put into operation there will be a predictable result. In chemistry, if two elements, sodium and chlorine, are brought together in the proper proportions the result is salt. The devastation area of the atomic bomb was worked out in advance and set down in a precise mathematical formula. When the bombs were dropped on Japan, the devastation occurred according to the formula. Physical scientists do not anticipate anything else but that the application of a given cause will produce the sequence of a given effect.

While we know far less about psychological laws, there can be little doubt that the workings of cause and effect are just as immutable as in the domain of the physical

sciences. Some psychiatrists believe that if you ask someone to name a flower and he replies, "lily," it is the only
answer he could have made at that instant. Everything
that happened previously in the life history of that individual will be in some measure, however slight, focused
upon producing the response "lily" instead of "rose" or
"orchid" or some other flower.

Whether or not this is true, we may be sure that the
emotional and social patterns sketched into the personality during childhood will be elaborated and, while they
will be camouflaged, nevertheless they will stand out in
bold behavior relief when the children become adults.
Perhaps there may be cataclysms of personality due to
very strong emotional influences in early adult life, which
may reverse the cause-and-effect behavior formula, but
these are scarcely frequent enough to change appreciably
the general average.

Therefore, it is reasonable and logical to state that the
seeds implanted by the mother during childhood will in
adult life bear a good harvest of emotional growth and
expansion and of social responsibility. The few good
seeds that moms may sow are soon choked off by the
lush weed growth of selfishness, by a minimum of giving
and a maximum of taking, by the clinging to lower,
childish, dependent stages rather than progressing to
higher independent levels. There are yielded a few scraggy
and unhealthy emotional plants and the unripe fruit of
social irresponsibility. The cause is definite. Generally the

effect is predictable and sadly irreversible. A great poet uttered an eternal verity when he said, "For children, the voice of parents is the voice of God."

Undoubtedly man will always retain strong self-protective and assertive behavior drives. In view of the significant role played by self-preservation in man's long and bloody struggle for survival it could hardly be otherwise. However, as time passed, the stark reality of primary selfishness was somewhat relieved and modified by the security resulting from the greater strength of numbers of human beings—groups gathered together for a common purpose. Later, much later, thinking and behavior were influenced by man's most recent psychological acquisition—the super-ego. The super-ego comprises not only higher intelligence, but also it makes it possible, and indeed sometimes obligatory, for a man to stand off from himself and survey his own conduct. If it falls too far short of the ideal of what he would like it to be, he experiences self-blame and guilt. This aspect of the super-ego roughly corresponds to conscience. In mob action and in war, where men act in groups, each man decreases his feeling of personal blame, either for the illegal killing of a lynching mob or the socially sanctioned murder of war, by merging his identity into that of the leader. In this way, the leader becomes responsible for the killing and the individual at least escapes the heaviest impact of self-blame. Frequently, too, the super-ego stirs men to rise beyond their baser selves and behave in an altruistic and self-sacrificing manner.

In every human being there is at least some tinge of loyalty and regard for his family. Sometimes it soars to peaks of idealism, life being abandoned so that another in the family might survive. In the sinking of the *Titanic* there were many such epics of human behavior. Men placed their loved ones, their wives and children, in the life boats, and then stood on the deck of the fast sinking ship, waiting to be submerged by the icy sea. In every catastrophe, there are examples of human behavior at its noblest.

Again, in almost every human being at some time in his life, there is at least a trace of feeling for the state, the land of his birth or adoption. Sometimes, too, this segment of self reaches for the skies and we view with awe the kind of patriot who is saddened because he has only a single life to give to his country. The war has added many such patriots to our national list of immortals.

Finally, in the majority of men there is a speck (too often, ultramicroscopic) of feeling for all men, not so much for humanity en masse because they have suffered grievously from war or some other catastrophe, but a feeling for men as human beings, a bond of sameness under the skin which is the essence of the true brotherhood of man.

Undeniably even in the best and most mature men and women, the veneer of internationalism is very thin. Internationally we are social pygmies—isolationists at heart.

Very immature men and women have practically no sense of international social responsibility, but even the attainment of a high level of personal emotional-social maturity does not add much to our growth as citizens of the world. In one sense, it may even inhibit such growth. On the surface, the needs and demands of self, the family, and the nation, are in conflict with the needs and demands of the world at large. In order to give to the one it would appear we must take from the others. We ask, "Where did the food come from that we are sending to the farthest corners of the world?" It must come from the supply which may be needed for ourselves and our families. "If affiliations and alliances with foreign nations are made, does it not mean that alien standards of living and customs will permeate our national structure and endanger our American way of life?" Superficially the argument is valid enough. Definitely we are a "have" nation, and at this writing, the larger area of the earth is inhabited by "have not" nations. It would seem we have very much to lose and very little to gain. Perhaps this is the reason our societal vision is myopic. Actually, the sufferings of millions of poor Chinese and other millions of "untouchables" in India are very real and horrible, but, viewed from across thousands of miles, they are blurred by unreality.

Even though we are a "have" nation, we *do* have a great deal to lose by holding aloof from world affairs. There are very practical reasons for keeping in close contact with international politics. The world is rapidly shrinking in size. I flew across the Atlantic in twenty hours, and that was slow flying time. Army airmen have flown from Los Angeles to New York in less than four hours and a quarter. Leo T. Crowley in his report to the Senate stated that the military defeat of the Nazis was due to the disruption of their transportation by bombing and the destruction of a few key supplies, such as aircraft ball bearings and fuel, and not by destroying the major part of their general industrial plant. "It appears that if the Germans could have held out only six months longer they would have been able to smash New York City with improved V-2 bombs." So there is a selfish reason why we should be very familiar with what is happening in the world in which we live, even in its remote outposts. The idealistic reasons are far from visionary. A democracy which cannot cross the frontiers of its own nationalism is not of the essence of true democracy, and eventually it will not be a democracy at all.

Our social perspectives are limited even for short distances. If we happen to live on the Atlantic seaboard we are only mildly concerned by the news of a terrific storm on the West Coast with loss of life and enormous property damage, or of a destructive "twister" in the Midwest. But unless a member of the family is visiting in one of those areas or we own property there, we are much more affected as we listen with undivided and rapt attention to a radio broadcast of storm signals along the Atlantic Coast. During a very hot summer in Philadelphia, where I live, something went wrong with the water system and the water supply was shut off from one area of the city. Practically every person who mentioned it to me said in effect, "I am glad we don't live in that part of town." About one in five added as an afterthought that "in this boiling weather it must be rather bad for the people who do live there."

A little child is stricken with infantile paralysis. A mother who is a good neighbor and has a little boy the same age is genuinely sorry, but her deepest emotional reaction is fervent thanks that "it wasn't little Jackie who came down with polio." She even had a passing thought (of which she is promptly ashamed) of being glad it wasn't the little boy across the street, with whom Jackie plays so nicely, who was stricken.

All this is natural and human. However, it does indicate that the milk of human kindness is first strained through the filters of self, of family, of home, and of nation, and what comes through for the Chinese, the Indians, and other far-off unfortunates is pretty thin skimmed milk.

Children in their communion with each other are often remarkably altruistic in their plans and behavior. When misfortune, sickness, or death visits the family of one of their playmates I have observed children to give examples of practical sympathy and understanding which sometimes shamed the clumsy efforts of adults. Children may propose very thoughtful solutions to their mothers. If there is sickness in Mary Lou's house and her mother is worn out with overwork or worry, it may be suggested that "we have" Mary Lou's young brother and sister "stay with us for a while." Or, perhaps, Sally's mother is "terribly sick" and only a part-time nurse could be secured, "Mother, I won't be home for dinner. We are taking turns looking after Sally's mother and it is my turn this afternoon and evening."

The altruism of children divides itself into two categories—that promoted by various organizations and that which is more or less spontaneous with the children themselves. The latter is much more significant for the social development of children.

Usually moms are not averse to more or less general altruism, like saving pennies for the heathen children—"The poor things don't even know there are homes like ours." Or making up Christmas baskets for poor children —"I couldn't bear it if you children didn't have a perfect Christmas."

When it comes to more personal things like being friendly and companionable to a child in school who is of a different race or color, moms are apt to be very dubious: "After all, darling, he (or she) is so very different. He won't understand and will take advantage of your kindness. I am sure the families of your best friends won't like it. I wish you wouldn't."

Generally, mothers give much more latitude and have a longer perspective. I know a Japanese painter who is either a genius or very close to one. His art is recognized by notable institutions and by fellow artists. He is not interested in the many opportunities to commercialize his art and paints only what he wants to paint. Consequently he has had to subsist on the smallest of pittances.

When the war came he was bewildered. He is probably sixty years old and has been in this country since childhood. He has lost all contact with Japan. The FBI cleared him and allowed him reasonable leeway, but naturally he was the recipient of a certain amount of unfriendly public attention.

A woman who has known him for many years offered him the shelter of her home. Her two half-grown daughters were a bit squeamish about the idea at first. Apparently they had encountered some criticism in the community in which they lived. The mother, however, carried on naturally and easily, as though it were a commonplace, everyday procedure. The Japanese fitted into the home unobtrusively, and among the thanks he shyly offered were beautifully done sketches of the home scenes, the family and friends, the dog and the cats. These sketches were an unfailing source of joy to the son of the house serving in the South Pacific. Soon the two daughters accepted the arrangement, were enthusiastic about it, and happy to participate in it. I believe that the international social stature of these two children has grown appreciably.

All in all, the sons and daughters of mothers come through childhood with a much higher potential for becoming citizens of the world than do the children of moms. I believe that some time, and in the not too distant future, such citizens of the world will be critically important. Again the time will come when world combat will threaten. If it should come to another world war, the result might very well be the annihilation of our civilization

and cultures and the final plunge into the abyss of bar-
barism. When that danger comes, those adults who, in
their childhoods, were taught to take at least a few steps
along the road of the brotherhood of man will be the
human dikes holding back the deluge.

CHAPTER XV

J'ACCUSE

Earlier in this book, when discussing the causes of moms, I laid the blame on the moms who raise moms, on responsibility-shirking husbands, sexual frustration, and general emotional immaturity. These, however, are merely the immediate causes. The basic, underlying cause is the social system under which mom is allowed to flourish and flower. If I have been hard on mom and her surrogates, she can find solace in the unending hymn of praise that the system provides. Actually, the system deserves the more severe indictment.

Moms fit snugly and wholeheartedly into the social order as it has evolved in our matriarchy. The community applauds and admiringly smiles upon them. Therefore, there is no urge for them to examine their records as mothers. The society in which they move judges them by deceptive surface appearances. Often they are spoken of as "giving their lives" for their children. Hidden from public view, however, is the hard and tragic fact that for the lives "they give" for their children, in return either directly or—even more destructively—indirectly, they exact in payment the emotional lives of their children. Usually moms are paid in full.

The system which makes use of mom has given her enormous political power. She has natural vote-getting appeal. In the language of the politician, she has "given so much" and "she asks for so little." Actually she asks for more than the nation can afford to give—the sacrifice of the maturity of the new generation and the loss of the hope of its youth becoming participating and contributing citizens.

Should the audience of a political orator become unresponsive, then no matter what he happens to be talking about he can save the situation and call forth resounding bursts of applause if he proclaims that the hand that rocks the cradle makes the fiber of the nation. The applause would be somewhat less enthusiastic if he added a "but" to the effect that there are too many moms who are not really mothers and that the immaturity they are busily and selfishly indoctrinating in their children will be a peril to the nation rather than a protection. The applause would subside altogether and the candidate would lose votes, should he dare conclude that, if this kind of mom continues to increase and multiply, then we might face defeat should there be the catastrophe of another war or even now should we fail to achieve the goal of a democratic peace.

If a person invents something or makes something, he or she usually is held responsible, partly at least, for how the product turns out. If a man makes a mouse trap which does not catch mice, both he and the trap will be criticized. Certainly the inventor will not be praised for cluttering the market with another useless contraption. When a real mother bears a child, no one need tell her she has incurred a responsibility. She knows it and demonstrates her willing acceptance of the responsibility by her everyday behavior. Only the mom escapes scot-free.

When, as frequently happens, a youngster becomes antisocial or even criminal, public judgment rationalizes the issue. Almost never is the mom (or the system which produced her) tried in the Court of Public Opinion along with her delinquent son or daughter. Instead, the mom is profoundly pitied.

Personally, I believe that general education, particularly progressive education, certainly in its ultra-modern aspects, should be indicted as a part of the mom-fostering system. I realize that I am taking sides on a very moot question. Many eminent schoolmen will completely disagree, but as many more will be in agreement. Included will be such well-known school teachers as William Owen, now principal of the Consolidated School of Barryton, Michigan. He was an enthusiastic supporter of progressive education. For years, he believed in the new system and worked to advance it. Today he does neither.

There is no doubt that progressive education rescued the educational system from the doldrums. The authority in the schoolroom had been too rigid, almost Prussian. The fear of failure in classes was very grim. There was undeviating attention to the material in the textbooks and there was no real bid for the overall interest of the child. Bright children progressed not according to their mental preparedness and development, but were held back by reason of their ages and sizes. On the other hand, if the behinds of the laggards were too big for their seats, they might be promoted to a grade where the seats were larger. Progressive education corrected these and other things, but it overcorrected them.

The balance between individual self-expression and behavior was not only modified, as was badly needed, but it was explosively shattered. I believe there is only one way of becoming a wise and constructive non-conformist in adult life and that is by early practice and experience in conforming. Mental hospitals are filled with young patients who insisted on trying radical short cuts to nonconformity. Many youngsters, particularly boys, who in the first year or two of school life give interesting and promising evidences of self-expression, at the ages of ten to fifteen and later are unruly. "Insubordinate" would better describe their behavior, but the use of the word has been tabooed by progressive education. In the higher brackets of progressive education, in order to control the class the teacher was supposed to convey deli-cate hints to the pupils and to encourage good example by his or her controlled behavior. No doubt it worked—*sometimes*. No doubt, too, more often it did not work. The children were too busily engaged in noisily express-ing themselves, to observe that the teacher also was hope-fully self-expressing.

Complete independence and absolute freedom of emo-tional thought and behavior are a myth. If such qualities could exist they would be a grotesque anomaly. All through our lives it is necessary that we retain a minimal amount of emotional reliance upon others, upon ideas, upon ideals. Unconsciously children are confused and resent the complete removal of the milestones of teacher guidance and control.

Advanced progressive education strives to eliminate competition. It says there shall be no rewards for success and no penalties for failure. Class standing is abolished so that no child shall feel humiliated or pained by the knowledge that another child is handling the academic work better than he. It is interesting and Utopian, but, unfortunately, it is not life and it is not sound preparation for life. Life is still very much a matter of stiff competition, very often cruel and ruthless. It involves the striving for success and the enjoyment of its rewards, the facing of failure and the payment of its penalties. It is easy enough to change the criteria of success. The criterion need not be money. It can be power or honor or recognition and appreciation. At the current cross-roads of our cultures, however, it must be something. Communistic governments in countries where money is relatively unimportant soon learned that it was impossible to function without discriminating recognition. In the last analysis, in communistic systems, there is a wider gulf between the speed-up capacity worker and the average one than there is at the assembly belts of Detroit and other great industrial centers of our capitalistic economy.

In Russia the name of the top speed factory worker became the synonym for working efficiency. The worker was a national hero—which is recognition, money or no!

It is to the credit of progressive education that it abolished the brutal schoolroom competition often stimulated by teachers. Some children were hopelessly broken and crushed and became life-long casualties of inferiority. However, there is good reason to believe that progressive education went too far. It looks not only as if the penalty for failure was removed, but also that much of the desire and incentive to achieve was erased as well. If this were generally true, it would be unfortunate for the children and for the nation. It might be tragic.

All in all, it would seem fair to conclude that the pendulum of progressive education swung too far to the left. It is now swinging back. I think it will come to a stop somewhere to the left of center but nearer to conservative than to ultra-modern progressive education.

I am still very much worried about those hundreds of thousands of young Americans who could not serve in this war because they were militarily ineffective, the cause of which was often diagnosed as psychoneurosis. I wish I knew more about the ingredients that went into the making of the ineffectiveness. There was a large amount of mom, but there were other things, too. Perhaps it is merely a coincidence, but the peak of progressive education was reached about 1930. The majority of the school children of that time would have been at the military age for this world war. I would very much like to know how many of the psychoneurotic-ineffectives had been exposed to progressive education.

At a cursory glance, progressive education would seem to be opposed to the principles and practices of momism. Theoretically, it is designed to promote a rapid flowering of maturity. It advocates independence of behavior. It opposes emotional dependency. It urges individual selection of interests. It scoffs at rewards and punishments. In fact, progressive education would appear to damn all the instruments and devices by which momship maintains its sovereignty.

Nevertheless, I think there is a kinship between the techniques of progressive education and momism. They both produce a spurious maturity. In both the authority is heavily veiled. It cannot be seen, but it is there. The authority bargains for something that has the semblance of maturity, but really is immaturity. The terms of the bargain seem to be very generous. Large behavior concessions are granted. In progressive education, behavior restrictions and penalties for misbehavior are largely removed in the hope that self-expression will be favored and hastened. Progressive education operates on a much higher level than does mom, though no doubt she feels that what she, too, is doing is for the child's good. She bargains on a low level. In order to conceal the growth-restricting control of loving-dominance she concedes extensive behavior territories. This lends the appearance of unrestricted freedom of thought and conduct—almost unique unhampered self-expression. For instance, punishment may be waived and fear of consequences magically dispelled for surreptitiously taking dad's car, driving without a license, colliding with another car, and incurring a heavy bill for damages. Should the law step in, dad is bullied by argument and tears into using influence and whisking the culprit beyond the law's clutches. Should William fall too far below the school's academic standards, mom successfully pleads the case with his teachers and by dint of promises and threats, and perhaps by employing a tutor, she makes it possible for William to continue his ardent tooting of the saxophone. Jack, who is well beyond the age of childhood fantasy, tells elaborate and fantastic lies. Mom is entranced by his "powers of imagination" and successfully foils his father's attempts to cultivate truthfulness. Much of this self-expressive behavior involves youngsters in situations which are ominous and threaten retaliations and punishments. Mom is the indefatigable and omnipotent Protectress, the invulnerable fortress between the child and the consequences of his behavior. But for the child's future it is a vicious circle. The more "self-expressive" the youngster's behavior becomes, the more he needs mom's protection; and the more she gives it, the tighter she draws the leading strings.

Without the support of the system which created her, mom would be a hopelessly weak creature and would not long survive. She is so strong because she is fed constantly on unlimited and undiscriminating public praise and flattery: the approval of husbands who do not wish to be disturbed in their masculine pursuits by participating in the psychological development of the children; flattery by society which, in order to save itself the trouble of finding a satisfactory place in the community for middle-aged and frustrated wives, approves her momish behavior. In a certain measure, too, she receives the benediction of progressive education. Without these various supports mom would topple from her throne.

CHAPTER XVI

HOW CAN WE HELP MOM?

What are we to do about it? The problem is one of combating the cause rather than the effect. I'm afraid there's little that can be done for the older moms—their work is done. But we can make an effort to educate the mothers and fathers to be. Unfortunately, a full-fledged mom or pop is rather thickly insulated against education by the very conditions that made them what they are.

Repeatedly in the course of my professional life I have carefully explained to many women in the interests of their children, who were my patients, the dangers of momism. All in all, the results have not been too encouraging. In most cases, the impression I made on moms was neither deep nor lasting. It was not difficult to obtain agreement with everything I said, but unfortunately the business of being a mom is not one of thinking but of *feeling,* and feelings etched in deeply by years of practice are hard to eradicate.

Some years ago I had as a patient a boy who was close to the borderline of schizophrenia and in imminent danger of crossing into it. His mother's attitude toward him was extremely important in my efforts at treatment. Painstakingly I explained the situation to her and told why, when she visited her son at the sanitarium, she must not baby him as she had done by saying such things as, "Don't worry, lamb, momsie will make you all well. Come back to mommie soon, sweet, she needs you."

I thought the woman understood my explanation. She was a college graduate and intelligent. She agreed that she would not repeat her offense and thanked me for my instructions with tears in her eyes.

In spite of all this, her visits continued to be sentimental lullabies in which she crooned her son closer and closer to the land of unreality from which I was trying to hold him back. Finally, I had to forbid her visits. Immediately she removed the boy from my care. I kept track of the subsequent happenings. First, there followed a quest for a psychiatrist who would subscribe to the belief that her "mother love" could save her boy. She could not find one, so she took him to the country with a nurse whom she could dominate and treated him herself.

Today, the boy is in a mental hospital, hopelessly insane. His mom cannot visit him now. At the sight of her he flies into a homicidal rage and has to be mechanically restrained. In the violent language of his mental disease, he refers to her as "that angel of death who puts poison in my food and drains away my sexual strength."

By becoming just a bit of a mother, that mom could have saved her boy. In trying to save him for herself, she lost him. Most moms are rather impervious to advice or criticism. Blinded by their "smother love," they simply cannot see that they are wrong and are harming their children.

The answer lies, not in revamping the moms, but in revamping the system.

For the welfare of the nation, it is high time that women and men should expect and should be expected to give evidence of fulfilling the obligations and responsibilities of parenthood. There is no reason why the institution of motherhood should not be investigated and evaluated just as any other institution, the Republican and Democratic parties, the medical profession, labor, or major league baseball—indeed any occupation or institution. The nation has a far greater stake in the occupation of motherhood than in any other. I trust that some time in the not-too-distant future it will no longer be necessary to approach the subject with soft and reverent tread and to inquire in a hushed voice how the business of motherhood is progressing.

I doubt if we will ever reach such a level of honesty that the Army will return to his mother a son who was inadequate and ineffective in military service, with a report like this: "We are returning your son to you. We cannot make a soldier of him. In fact, we do not believe anything useful can be made of him by anyone. If we kept him in the Army we would have to assign two good soldiers to coddle him. He has not changed at all. He is still as much a baby as when you nursed him and changed his diapers."

I doubt if it will be ever possible for a mature wife to return her immature husband to his mom with a note along this general line: "I am returning your son to you. I am afraid it was never intended that he should be a husband. I have three healthy, normal children and I intend to keep them that way. I cannot do this if I permit your son to stay in this house. Besides, the three children keep me busy and I do not have the time to look after another child. Your son is too old and too large to be a baby and as a child he is not very attractive. He cannot even play with the children because he is too easily offended. But you will not have any trouble with him. He misses you very much and I am sure he will be much happier with you than he has been with me and the children."

While we may never attain such frankness, yet if we succeed only in dispelling the atmosphere of sentimentalism which envelopes motherhood, then, at least, we may hope to arrive at a common-sense level where praise will be given where praise is due and blame where blame is due, let the chips fall where they may.

That part of the elaborate façade concealing the dangers of momism which has been built by selfish husbands should be demolished. Whether the pretense be devotion to business or profession or whether it is on the lower level of stag pleasures and interests, it is the evasion of the time and trouble necessary to make that contribution to the maturing of children, particularly boys, which only the father can make. I know some husbands whose only contribution to the functions of fatherhood seems to consist of frequent and deep libations drunk at convivial male gatherings to the "fine little woman who is at home taking care of the children." The wife is left holding the bag—an empty bag—and if she has any of the makings of immaturity, she is likely to fill that bag with deep and dangerous emotional attachments to her children, which take the place of those her husband has tossed aside. No man, whether he be the executive of a huge corporation or a humble laborer, has the right to evade his plain duty toward his children and his participation with his wife in the performance of that duty.

How can we go about laying a better foundation for parenthood? First of all, by educating and preparing our boys and girls to be mothers and fathers. In girls' schools, we have endless courses in cookery, sewing, and baby-care, but none in the serious business of being a real mother. The same situation exists in boys' schools: carpentry, economics, and athletics, but not a word on father-hood. Maturity might well be the subject of a course included in our high-school and college curricula. Such instruction could scarcely be begun too early or continued too long. Not only would we be training future parents, but the students would be given a true insight into the tricks of momism and would detect the subterfuges of moms and stubbornly resist them.

Secondly, we should correct the defect in our social system which militates against the mother and adds dubious prestige to the mom. It is made somewhat too difficult for women, particularly married women, to participate fully in civic affairs. Yet it would be impossible to imagine anyone whose experiences would be more fruitful and whose counsel would be wiser than those of a well-adjusted wife and mother. She knows the needs of children, certainly the paramount consideration of the nation. The mother who has been frustrated in her marriage, but nevertheless has been strong and determined enough not to lower her ideals of motherhood is splendid material for participation in public affairs. She refuses to compensate for her marital frustration by crippling her children with emotional overattachments. Therefore she has much to give to the community which would be helpful to others and notably to children. The defect which denies the right kind of women total participation in political and other activities should be corrected by educating public opinion.

I doubt that mothers were consulted before progressive education was put into effect. Irrespective of whether progressive education eventually will prove to be valuable or not, it is still important that intelligent mothers, who have children in school, should be familiar with proposed changes in educational systems and their opinions should be taken into consideration. As it stands now, the moms are much more vociferous than the mothers. They are strongly activated by personal interest and bias. They can be entirely conscienceless about attempting to have a competent teacher officially beheaded if they feel their children have been slighted. Mothers are much more hesitant. Unless the matter is quite serious and there has been manifest unfairness, they hesitate to take sides. For one thing, they know that later on in life children are bound to encounter a certain amount of unfairness and they should learn in advance to meet and discount it.

The wall that protectively camouflages the mom is doomed to fall, but anything which will speed its demolition would be very welcome. There are some hopeful and promising stirrings. The nursery school movement is excellent. In the free and natural play life of young children, there is the breaking down of inhibitions and the first faltering, but significant, steps toward maturity. Parent-teachers groups have made a considerable contribution and lay mental hygiene organizations have conducted reasonably successful programs of public education concerning the psychological needs of children.

One program, originated in a church in Schenectady, New York, is being taken up by other churches throughout the country. Some time ago Schenectady's Reformed Church, with the help of psychologists from Union College, started a school designed to overcome its students' fear of failure, their distrust of their own abilities, and to build self-confidence and maturity. From all reports this program is meeting with good success and the idea is spreading. Basically, the program is one of teaching maturity.

A few colleges are now offering down-to-earth courses in sex and adult living. One of the most notable of these is the "youth and marriage course" conducted at the

University of California at Berkeley. Under able leadership, sex becomes an open classroom topic with few punches pulled. More colleges should follow this plan.

These efforts must not only be expanded, but those conducted by lay groups must have continuous and sensible psychiatric monitoring. Lay groups are always in danger of acquiring "lunatic fringes" and of being taken over by mom and her surrogates. There is even danger of mom being grossly deceived and shamelessly used by some unscrupulous and evil organizations. So-called "mother groups" often are fertile ground for the breeding of propaganda for national disunity, distrust, and defeatism. During the war, the Nationalist Party is said to have had control of mother groups in twenty-two of our largest cities including Cleveland, Philadelphia, Washington, Chicago, Detroit, Cincinnati, and Los Angeles. Under "expert guidance" they adopted resolutions that the war be stopped immediately, that we try our government officials for starting the war, that conscription be prohibited, and that the Federal Reserve System be abolished. It does not require the experienced eye of a psychiatrist to recognize the handiwork of misguided and exploited moms.

Moms, being much more emotionalized and personalized than mothers, are far less thoughtful and wary and the more likely to fall into these pitfalls. Mom has an unerring instinct for emphasizing the immediate, the personal, and the unusual, together with an amnesia for the general welfare of children. Often, for instance, when she is so articulate about the tremendous uplifting value of esthetic dancing for children, or exclaims so oratorically against the shameless way sex is taught in the schools, she is being moved by some immediate difficult situation regarding her own offspring. Underneath there is always that ever-present conscious anxiety that her children may be taken away from her emotionally.

We have gone a long way toward cutting down the yearly toll due to cancer, tuberculosis, and venereal diseases by a three-fold program—talking about them freely, presenting the cold hard facts for all to see, and continuous unrelenting public education. The same program could be applied to the threat of moms. Once we can talk about the subject openly, *and loudly,* one of the main hurdles will be cleared—more and more people will learn to recognize the dangers. Public education, particularly in colleges, high schools, and even in grade schools, is tremendously important. I cannot say too much about the role that our teachers can play. We cannot do a great deal for the dyed-in-the-wool mom herself unless she is willing to cooperate; but we can help the children of moms to break their silver cords, we can help them to grow up emotionally, we can help them to find the road toward real motherhood and fatherhood rather than the bewildering path to unreal momhood and pophood.

There is one thing we must remember: Immature, selfish moms produce sons and daughters who are usually not capable of making more than an indifferent economic return and are largely incapable of more than a futile social gesture. They occupy an area of our democracy purely as "squatters." Real mothers produce men and women who till and cultivate our national soil—economically and socially. If the moms increase disproportionately at the expense of mature mothers, then there is real danger that the nonproductive "squatters" will dispossess the contributing and constructive citizens of our democracy with the result that our nation will be greatly weakened.

CHAPTER XVII

WHAT MOM CAN DO ABOUT IT

What can mom do about it? She can do a great deal if she is not too completely immature and is able and willing to recognize her true self and try. Unfortunately, markedly immature people seldom see their own shortcomings.

No doubt mothers who have read this book this far agree with much that I have written. Some may be surprised that I have not said more. They are mothers. They know much more about children than I do. No mere man can ever hope to understand more than a slight fraction of the inner workings of motherhood. A male obstetrician may be profound in his deep understanding of labor and expertly skilled in the bringing of babies safely into this world, but he can never understand the "feeling" of making and having a baby. That feeling is reserved for women.

Likewise, no matter how large his psychological understanding of mothers and children, a man can only remotely comprehend the deep inner conflicts and powerful driving forces which impel a real mother first to protect and **hold** her baby, then to free it from herself. Unless a woman is abnormal or mentally sick, it is easy and natural for her to guard and defend her child. Unfortunately, however, the rejecting or emancipating function, so instinctive in animals, is difficult for many women. They have produced something and they want to continue to hold it.

They are the moms, and the moms who have read this far will be angry. I should expect them to be. Somewhat mischievously I might suggest that their ire will be in direct ratio to the amount of momishness that is in them. I hope they will be very angry, because the natural repercussion of their anger should be to defend themselves and exclaim, "Well, if you think you know so much, why don't you tell us what to do about it?"

If the moms should say this I would be grateful. I would regard it not only as an invitation, but as an opportunity and even a mandate. Of course, the way to stop being a mom is to stop being one, but there are helpful explanations and criteria.

The various schools of thought concerning the psychology of children often disagree in theory and techniques, but each one worth its psychological salt has the same objective—the accomplishment for children of a sound and enduring emotional and social maturity, so that, without too great strain and without too many difficulties, the conditions and problems of adult life may be met and solved with reasonable success. Maturity, in any case, is the goal.

At least we can be sure of a few simple facts. We know there are children. We know, too, that they live and move about in certain surroundings which we call their environment. It would be silly to study children without reference to their environments. Environments become all the more significant when it is realized that children do not make them and only in very small degree can they control them. It is obvious that something very important must happen as a result of the contact between the child and its environment. For one thing, such contact involves physical factors that have a very definite effect upon the child's body—food with its important vitamins, sunlight, fresh air, the opportunity to move about freely, and many other things. If the supply of these things should be insufficient or shut off altogether, the effect would be disastrous—a serious slowing up or crippling of the physical growth and development of the child and even death.

Just as the child must draw upon its environment for the satisfaction of its physical needs, so also must it depend upon it for the satisfaction of its emotional needs and emotional growth. In this connection, it must be kept in mind that the important content of the environment of children consists of other human beings. For young children these are notably the parents and most significantly the mother. If there is an insufficient supply of psychological food, or if it is of the wrong kind, then the emotional life of the child will be seriously damaged, possibly even destroyed.

It is convenient to have a name for what is built into the child from that which it derives both physically and mentally from the particular environment in which it lives. It is called personality. A dramatic but valid way of looking at the personality of a boy or girl approaching adult life is to realize that it is a condensed but exact record of *everything* that has happened during childhood, including the reactions to the multitude of experiences in life, large and small, trivial or critical. A pattern has been set. In the making of that pattern, the parents have been more instrumental and more determining than any one or anything else. The bequest of parents to children of material possessions is far less important than the legacy of sound, mature, well-integrated, flexible personalities.

Children may be viewed objectively and their behavior classified into "good" or "bad," according to whether experience proves that the pattern of behavior laid down in childhood proves helpful or harmful in their adult life. Look at the spoiled child, and particularly let the mom look thoughtfully at the child she is spoiling. Without inquiring into why and how the child is being spoiled, it is clear that when later on in life that child attempts to dominate an unsympathetic environment by the behavior of a spoiled child, a method which was successful in childhood, he or she encounters rebuffs, disappointments, and frustrations that lead to defeat in the struggle for emotional and social existence. If he wishes to survive he must "unspoil" himself. It is extremely difficult and painful to erase a deeply ingrained behavior pattern and substitute a new one which is its direct opposite.

Even before its birth, there is in every living thing a potential or innate possibility and promise for growth and development. Since it operates so mysteriously it might be called the "X" quantity. See how beautifully it functions in the growth of the physical structure of a child. When the baby-to-be is in the womb of the mother, its various organs and parts at first are so undifferentiated that only an expert can tell what is going to be what— liver, spleen, spinal cord, fingers, toes, teeth. However, the buds of these organs, nourished by the same blood, grow into organs and tissues, vastly different from each other. It would seem that there existed in the organ buds, the power of selecting from the blood the proper kind and in the proper amount, those factors that will insure normal growth. After birth, the baby is still quite incomplete with a small nervous system, tiny organs, muscles, and bones, eyes that cannot focus, legs that cannot walk, vocal chords that cannot speak, and many other parts that function only very partially.

Again the doctrine of the "X" potential operates, and from the blood-nutrition delivered to this small but compact structure, seemingly there is selected what is needed to produce eventually, full-grown organs and parts, each one being quite different in structure and function, but interlocking and working together to constitute the smoothly working machinery of the human body. An interesting comparison may be made. If there is the physical potential for maturity, likewise there is a potential or "X" quantity which works toward the attainment of emotional and social maturity and security. The chief purpose of emotional growth in any child is to give it the opportunity to make for itself a workable personality, so that the conditions and demands of adult life may be met satisfactorily, so that the child may have an even chance of meeting his fellow men on even terms, finding satisfaction and happiness in life and standing up to its rebuffs. At least, we have some idea of the nature of the psychological potentials which soon show themselves in children. I repeat that since the shaping of childhood environment is largely in the hands of adults and particularly parents, it is *the* important obligation of parenthood to see to it that the environment contains in sufficient quantities those things that may be reasonably expected to bring the buds of the psychological potential into full flowering.

CHAPTER XVIII

DESIGN FOR CHILDHOOD

What are some of the factors which, when set in a background of love for the child, help in the making of a normal personality?

In the physical field, the problem is fairly easy. We know of the importance of fresh air, sunshine, cleanliness, the proper kind of food, exercise, and reasonable protection from disease. Unfortunately we know far less about the psychological needs; these are not so tangible.

There is no formula for building an emotionally normal child. If there were, India rubber might be the main ingredient, for a great deal of flexibility is needed. There are seven things, however, that a child must have if he is to grow into a mature adult: a desire to move, a readiness and willingness to imitate, an alert response to suggestion, a reasonable amount of the love of power, a strong leavening of curiosity, a dash of childhood savagery, and a spark of romancing. These important potentials must be satisfied to integrate the personality of a child and to build it satisfactorily. Properly handled and blended, they are the foundation stones of maturity.

In building a child's personality, the opportunity for physical motion must be provided and the inborn desire to move must be encouraged. That is how a child learns. A baby is largely responsive to sensation. It answers by a certain kind of response the stimuli that come through the route of the five ordinary senses—the stimulus of hunger, the stimulus of temperature differences, the stimulus of pain, and stimuli from various organs of the body demanding satisfaction.

An infant reaches out and crawls, explores its environment—not consciously, but instinctively. It comes into contact with the objects in its immediate surroundings with their similarities and differences in shape, size, consistency, texture, temperature, and many other properties. It "remembers" these things all the more deeply since the remembrance is not conscious but emotional. The importance of this motion is demonstrated by the rapidity of habit formation and elaboration in children —by the speed with which a baby progresses from the crawling stage to upright coordinated walking and the quickness with which it learns to avoid contact with sources of pain and danger.

You have probably heard a mother boast that her child is quiet and well-behaved. It is a stupid boast. Psychologically speaking, a quiet child is not a normal child. A quiet child is being deprived of the opportunity of getting its first growth of mind. The sensations that flow into the personality of a child through the route of motion are as necessary to its mental growth as the milk which it receives from its mother is for its physical growth. Encourage the desire for *motion* in your children, and, above all, allow that desire to continue into adulthood.

The second and probably the most important and dynamic psychological potential is *imitation*. It is important because here the child imitates mostly what is close to him—his mother and his father.

The ability to speak one's native language, aptly called the "mother tongue," is acquired largely through a process of imitation. The child hears certain sounds first from its mother, then from other adults in the vicinity. In the beginning the sounds are meaningless. Gradually there is an association between the sounds and the happenings that follow them. Thus they acquire meaning for the child and are repeated first as a word, then as a group of words.

The natural play life of children furnishes a striking example of the powerful influence of imitation. From time immemorial female children have taken pieces of cloth, old rags, or whatever they could lay hands on, and draped them around themselves in imitation of the skirts of their mothers. In playing house, children portray faithfully their parents' assets, but perhaps even more accurately, though noncritically, their faults. If it could be arranged it would be profitable, but not always amusing, for parents to listen in on their children's games. The mother might be somewhat startled to hear her little daughter, the play mother, whisper shrilly to the play maid after the doorbell "rings," "Annie, if that's Mrs. Jones tell her I am downtown shopping. I can't stand the old fool." Or the father might become somewhat reflective if he heard his voice accurately reproduced in miniature delivering a tirade liberally interlarded with profanity about that "so-and-so" who "swiped" the light bulb "from my reading lamp" or used his last razor blade to sharpen pencils.

The imitation of parents by children and in early life the imitation of the mother are the powerful twin driving forces of identification and idealization. One strengthens and reinforces the other. The parents are put on the highest pedestal of the ideal. Not only do the children pay them the tribute of imitation, but unconsciously they desire to merge themselves completely into them.

Children are pitifully weak and insecure. The more they can identify with, become a part of, their parents, the more freely can they borrow from them the emotional strength they need so much. And the higher the pedestal upon which they can place their parents, the greater the emotional security they can feel. So it is scarcely strong enough to say that children imitate their parents. Literally, they *must* imitate them.

There is a moral concerning imitation which applies not only to parents, but to every adult who is in contact with children—and what adult is not? The moral has a simple physical parallel. If we wish to save children from the tragedy of the weakling and send them out into life straight, healthy, and strong, then we must see to it that during childhood they are given the right physical conditions of life. If we wish to start their personalities in the right direction and prepare them for the most important issue in life—psychological maturity—then we must provide material to imitate, which when added together will reach that objective. This is a direct charge to all of us.

It would seem superfluous for parents and others to ask, "What shall we give children to imitate?" The surroundings should contain in liberal amounts those qualities, the imitation of which may be counted upon to build sound, mature, enduring personalities—honesty, straightforwardness, truthfulness, courage, reflection, judgment, decision, tolerance, patriotism, the outlines of a pattern of service to the community and the nation, and, since the world has become much more compact and accessible, at least some stirrings of internationalism. It seems like a large order, but these are only some of the specifications needed to make a citizen of the nation and the world. It is equally important that the early environment of children at least be relatively free from the opposite of these character-building attributes. In dishonesty, furtiveness, venal lying, cravenness, hasty action, ill-founded judgment, indecision, intolerance, selfish lack of patriotism, disregard of community and national needs, and a vacuum in place of any feeling of international responsibility, there is the composite of those termites who are striving so industriously to destroy the foundations of American democracy. The suitable pattern for the imitation of children to be wrought by parents and others might be expressed in a formula of daily

living in which there is at least a reasonable balance between taking and giving, between the acceptance of
privileges and the performance of duties.

The third important channel through which a considerable part of their surroundings flows into the molds
of children's personalities is *suggestibility*. Suggestibility
is an impetus or inclination toward this or that behavior
pattern, the stimulus being given by something, literally
anything, the child observes or senses in its environment.

Suggestibility is much more subtle than imitation. Imitation is direct and concrete—characteristics are there to
be imitated. A child sees an adult do something and,
because of the emotional significance of the adult in the
life of the child, the act becomes important and impres-
sive. Allowing for the difference between child and adult
in the capacity to perform, the child reproduces faithfully
what it has seen. Suggestibility is far less concrete and
direct. From the environment the child gets a certain
hint or clue, and it is likely to take that hint and behave
accordingly, particularly if the source of the suggestion
comes from the mother or the father. Normal children
literally drink in suggestions of all kinds from hundreds
of sources in the environments in which they live and
these suggestions over a period of time help to produce
the behavior patterns that shape their personalities.

The mother who, when her little daughter stumbles
and breaks a teacup, says to a visitor in the little child's
hearing, "Poor Betty, she is so nervous, just like her
father," is directly suggesting nervousness. If such harm-

ful suggestions continue the inevitable result may be predicted—a nervous child and, later, a nervous woman. A mother whose brother was a world-famous bridge-building engineer asked her ten-year-old son, "Bill, when you grow up, I suppose you are going to be a great engineer like your Uncle Stanley." Bill replied, "No, I guess I'm going to be a neurotic like my father." Bill's father invariably came to the breakfast table with an, "Oh, my head," and returned from his office in the evening with an, "Ouch, my back," frequently entertaining the family at dinner by explaining just how and why his various organs failed to perform satisfactorily.

Often a wise mother, treating her child who has been hurt, is the Master Physician. Indeed, sometimes she is more effective than some doctors, since she never neglects the physical-emotional or body-mind implications of the hurt, even though it may be merely a trivial bump or cut.

A child has tripped and bumped his head against the floor. Screaming, the youngster runs to his mother. Every mother's heart beats faster with apprehension when her child is hurt. Being a mother she knows or senses that any person's fears and particularly the fright of a child are somewhat allayed by a serious and careful examination of the injury. It is not good psychology to make light of it before examining it. Next the mother applies a remedy, even though it may not be much needed and may consist only of a cold compress. Again the mother realizes that even adults, but emphatically children, who have not the intelligence to reason out the trivial nature of an injury, need the magic of concrete treatment, something which "will make the hurt place feel better." The mother does all these things with reasonable calm, appreciating that between his screams, her youngster is scanning her face and feeling out her attitude for evidence that the hurt is "bad." In her bearing and by her words, the mother allays the fear of the child and suggests and inspires confidence and security. If she does not show alarm, then the alarm of Johnny or Sally soon subsides. The mother does not forget that not only the head but also the small and very sensitive ego of her child has been hurt and outraged. She sympathizes with the child, but does not descend into maudlin sympathy. Finally she blocks attempts to retreat into babyish immaturity and further soothes the ego by suggesting maturity—"I know it hurts, but it will be better soon and a man like you isn't going to cry about it." That is about all. It is enough —the simple and beautiful artistry of motherhood.

This same technique of suggesting growth and maturity can be used in endless ways to lead our children to adulthood. Suggestibility is a psychological weapon of great strength and usefulness in helping shape the personality of a child. It is flexible and double-edged. It must be used with bold strokes that will add worthwhile mature traits to character formation, and it must be turned broadside against any suggestion of those things which would jeopardize the building of a grown-up man or woman.

I doubt if ever there lived a normal man who, no mat-

ter how superior or indifferent he appeared to the attention and plaudits of his fellow men, did not prize his place
in the sun, even though it was only a very small place.
Inevitably it must be so, since the *love of power* begins
in childhood. Indeed, some psychoanalysts declare that
it originated when the child was in the womb of the
mother—so-called fetal omnipotence.

The childhood love of power is a more or less unconscious wish or drive to dominate the immediate surroundings. Within the limitations of preservation from harm,
usually everything is done to keep a baby satisfied, comfortable, and happy. The small piece of humanity does
not need any conscious process of reasoning to sense its
power over its environment. He soon learns to know
that making a certain kind of noise, called "crying," stimu-
lates the adults in the vicinity into fussing and scurrying
about energetically in their efforts to relieve an unpleasant
situation. It might be a pricking pin or a frightening
object it wants removed from the surroundings, like the
grinning gargoyle-like face of an uncle who is trying
to be friendly. Such scenes cannot be enacted day after
day without inducing in a baby an appreciation of power
and a desire to increase and retain it.

But baby dominance is all too short-lived. Too soon
comes the bitter disillusionment. The phase of happy,
irresponsible power over others must come to an end.
Annoying clothing must be worn. Table implements
must be used even though fingers are much more satisfactory for feeding and very fine for smearing. Property

belonging to others must be respected. No longer is it sufficient just to want something. The time must come when the child has to learn the painful lesson that adults and even other children have rights that must be respected and frequently conceded. Inevitably, in each child there comes the conflict between the demands of society, meaning at first his mother and the family circle, and the wish to retain and later regain the power of babyhood. Truly it is the tragedy of childhood, but it is part of the growing-up process that must be carefully handled by the parents.

We must be particularly wary of the psychologically critical situations that may follow in the wake of a serious childhood illness. Let us say there has been a lengthy, exhausting, and painful sickness, perhaps rheumatic fever. The illness comes to an end and convalescence begins. The child who has been so brave and relatively uncomplaining now behaves atrociously. The adults in the family try (and try too hard) to make up for the discomfort and pain the child has endured. The little patient is permitted to have his own way; his every whim is promptly gratified. Few normal children can withstand the temptation to reach back and attempt to grasp the golden apple of babyhood which has been kept beyond their reach since they were babies. Here is a situation requiring skillful management, a situation so critical that the wrong attitude may mar the whole future of the child.

In the home circle and in the schoolroom, children

may be observed seeking to regain the kingdoms of their babyhoods, striving to hold the center of the stage, by legitimate means if possible, but, if these fail, then by misconduct. Such was the situation in point brought to my attention recently:

Jack B. was a normal sturdy boy of seven, but he had one oddity, unusual in a healthy youngster. Occasionally he would come to the table and refuse to eat. Naturally his parents were concerned. They questioned him as to whether he was sick or worried or what it was that was wrong. Invariably Jack's answer was the same—"I'm all right. I just don't want to eat." Invariably, too, the dinner scene ended in the same way—Jack's mother in tears, his father angry, storming, threatening, and profane. Jack merely sat tight and did not eat. Finally Mr. and Mrs. B. consulted a psychiatrist. He listened carefully to the story, asked no questions and said, "My advice is that the next time this happens you do or say nothing." The parents were disappointed, but since they had paid a fairly large fee for the consultation, they decided to follow the psychiatrist's counsel. About a week later Jack came to the dinner table, politely declined food and announced that he did not intend to eat anything. His parents went on with the meal quietly conversing with each other and ignoring Jack. After a long silence, during which Jack failed to attract attention by squirming and other devices, he addressed his father—"Maybe you didn't hear me, Dad. I said I wasn't going to eat." His father replied, "Yes, Jack, we heard you. It is all right. It won't hurt a healthy boy like you to miss a meal." Jack was silent for a long time. Then suddenly he burst into tears, pounded on the table, and screamed at his parents, "Don't you hear me, Mother? I said I won't eat. Aren't you going to cry?" And to his father, "I said I won't eat, aren't you going to swear?" The father answered simply, "No, Jack. Now wouldn't you like to keep quiet and let us finish our dinner in peace?" Jack refused no more meals. This was his swan song, the final bid to reclaim the power of his baby days.

How should this critical developmental phase of childhood be managed? A common error is to overemphasize it by too much attention. It is a mistake to take either of two extreme attitudes. In one there is too much severity. The child is brought brutally face to face with the harsh fact that the days of power are over. He is punished severely for the least attempt to regain his baby domain. Many children who have been subjected to this extreme become so warped in their personalities that throughout their lives they remain frightened and defeated; others may project upon society the ill-usage they received during childhood and become bitterly anti-social and dangerous personalities. There is some reason to believe that, among the international gangsters who recently brought civilization to the brink of destruction, there were several whose inhumanity and sadistic cruelty were the revenge they exacted from society for the brutal treatment they received from their fathers when they were children.

The other extreme in handling the love of power is the spoiling process. Unwise and questionably kind adults often permit children to hang on to their babyhood power overlong. Sometimes this spoiling is pseudoscientifically camouflaged as "letting children express themselves." Often an only child, or perhaps a favorite child, is allowed to remain in the highly artificial position of continuing to exercise dominance. Other children are made to concede beyond all reasonable limits. Sometimes one or the other parent is forced to give in. Finally the day comes when the spoiled child must face the actual conditions of life. It is too late. He cannot conform. It is almost inevitable that he will be defeated by life. The habit pattern has been deeply inlaid. There are futile attempts reminiscent of childhood to gain the center of the stage, but the world counters by cold or cynical indifference. If he persists, there is active opposition and retaliation. The final result is either a bitterly disillusioned retirement from the world of adult emotional relationships or learning over a long period of time and in a sad and trying way a lesson that could have been learned with far less difficulty during childhood.

There is little doubt but that the human species is indebted for its survival to the fact that every normal child is an animated question mark. Were it not for the potential or X quantity of *curiosity* in human beings, we would have none of the benefits of modern life, from the wonder drugs penicillin and streptomycin to the gadgets in our homes. Science is simply applied curiosity. The real scientist is as curious as a child and his curiosity differs from that of a child chiefly in that the scientist has specialized information that gives purposeful direction to the eternal questioning in his mind. Beyond that, just like a child, he takes things apart and puts them together, whether it be matter or machinery, in order to see what makes them work.

The driving force of the curiosity of children is tremendous. Unless he wishes to lose his reputation for omniscience with his younger children, the tired father arriving home from his daily work may expect no respite from a barrage of such questions as, "If ducks can swim why can't chickens?" Or, "Why does our dog wag his tail when he is pleased, but our cat wags hers when she is cross?"

Only a small part of early education is supplied in school. The bulk of it comes from outside the formal confines of the schoolroom, answering the "why" almost continuously on the lips of children. So there is no escape for parents or, for that matter, anyone else who has intimate contact with children. The curiosity of the young should be and must be satisfied. It is dangerous to block it. If you have tried to shut off the flow of a brooklet by building an earth dam you know how other channels have been made by the force of the water to find an egress. This is exactly what happens to attempts to dam the curiosity of children. They find unsatisfactory and often harmful channels of information. The questions of young children must be answered simply, directly, and truthfully. Older children should be directed to available and authoritative sources of information. Knowledge acquired through personal effort adds significant layers to the personality.

Some parents, quite intelligent about their children, still balk at their manifestations of sex curiosity. They cannot accept the fact that it is normal for sex curiosity to be deeper and stronger than any other kind of curiosity. They are dismayed when their nice little boy wants to know about his own sex organs or the sex organs of his younger sister, and if they discover him examining them they are horrified.

The reasons are simple enough. Sex is one of the strongest of human traits, strong enough to be classed as an instinct. Naturally it begins to unfold early in life.

The second reason is an artificial one stupidly manufactured by adults—concealment. The subject of sex is clothed in mystery and, far too generally, out of bounds for children. Too often there is a hush-hush air when a child wanders into an adult discussion of sex. There is an abrupt silence and frantic gesturing and pointing at the little intruder. Always remember that curiosity, held back, checked, made difficult of satisfaction, is at once redoubled.

What should be done about sex curiosity? I do not think there should be formal lectures to groups of children. I believe the answer is to be found, chiefly, in the home atmosphere. If this is such that children do not hesitate to ask natural questions about sex, almost as readily as they ask other questions, then the right foundations are being laid for useful and helpful sex information. This is perhaps the most important environmental heritage that can be given to children. The "nervous breakdowns" of adult life are very complicated and difficult to unravel. In direct ratio to the symptoms, I believe they contain the aftermath of more ignorance, misinformation, and bad habit formation about sex than any other ingredient.

I know a man who has led a useful, contributing life, but a very unhappy one, in which there has been much anxiety, the cause of which he could not consciously fathom. He was ill at ease with his own children, and indeed was not comfortable in the presence of any children. Neither was he comfortable in the company of adults. A study of the situation revealed that, when he was a youngster, a brother ten years older than he discovered him masturbating and severely punished and deeply humiliated him. He is now about fifty years old and, at the beginning of his treatment, he had almost no remembrance of any of the happenings of his childhood. It was obvious that soon after his brother had shamed him he had experienced a wholesale repression, not only of that humiliation experience, but of almost all his childhood.

For parents and others there are available many sources of sex information suitable for children. Instruction in the comparative sex life of plants and animals, frequent visits to the zoo, and a few good books are valuable aids. Finally, for each parent it is good practice, from time to time as the opportunity presents, to have informal but frank talks with the children about sex. Begun in very simple fashion, such talks naturally will expand in complexity as the children grow older and they will be a source of increasing help and guidance. In this way much is added to the growing personality which in adult life will pay immense dividends in emotional health, security and happiness.

Some readers may think that I am making too much fuss about sex. I am not. Sex has been carried into our current civilization and culture with the gradual accumulation of more veneering, distortion, and perversion than any other human function, and yet it retains a more primitive basis than any other. Someone once said to me, "Why so much bother about sex? It is a natural function. Pigs don't have any trouble about sex." The answer is obvious: "Human beings are not pigs."

A sixth potential, through which a child's growing personality is fed, is *savagery*. Now that the tom-boy girl has been supplanted by the bobby-soxer who screams and swoons at the sound of "The Voice," savagery is much more common in boys than in girls. When I first began to practice psychiatry, my young male friends who were at this developmental phase usually wanted to go West to kill Indians. Sometimes they got several blocks away from their homes, after leaving kind but firm farewell notes for their parents. Some years later, boys wanted to be bandits or rum-runners. Now they aspire to being supermen.

What is childhood savagery? It has been thought to represent the condensed recapitulation of the long epoch of primitive savagery, one of the steps of the human species on the long way toward our present plane of civilization. Irrespective of its origin, however, it is an important phase of emotional growth, presenting an ideal opportunity for teaching love of nature and self-reliance and accumulating reserves of health and strength, which will be much needed later on in life.

I believe, too, that the phase of savagery is the time during which the spirit of competition should be developed. In my discussion of progressive education, I pointed out that there is a tendency in some of our schools to abolish all competition. I agree it is right to minimize it. Children should not be lashed to merciless rivalry. Nevertheless, I am inclined to think that later in life every child will meet situations that are best prepared for by fostering in childhood some desire to win. In adult life, as we live it, it is impossible to escape competition. In the games and activities of childhood, teach honesty, fair play, unwillingness to take unfair advantage, but leave to the child some satisfaction in victory. Modern life has recognized the claims and needs of savagery. There are boy scouts, summer camps, athletic competitions, and the like. These are normal outlets for "animal spirits."

Finally, there is a personality potential I call *romancing*. It is the telling of untruths that are not lies. Only if unduly prolonged does it become lying. Romancing is the budding of the imagination. In children it often comes out in the telling of tall tales to which Baron Munchausen's stories could not hold a candle. Never should romancing be brutally crushed. If, in effect, you say to a child, "That is a lie and you are a liar," then you are distorting or even destroying something potentially beautiful that is just beginning to grow. Children must be taught truthfulness, but it must be done gradually, tactfully, skillfully. For one thing, the romancing time is the time to introduce the child to good romantic literature. Here outlets and compensations will be found for the rapidly growing imagination.

It is best to adopt a middle-of-the-road policy toward the romancing of your children by not being too obviously and admiringly credulous. It may be true enough that the romancing of children contains some of that precious, cobwebby stuff of which great poetry is made, but there is no need to believe you have borne a genius. Statistics show that great liars are much more common than great poets. On the other hand, it is not wise to be too derisively skeptical of the adventurous stories you hear from your children. Probably romancing youngsters do not expect to be believed. They want and need an audience which will not scornfully humiliate and belittle them. If normal youthful imagination is turned back, deprived of its expressive words, there is danger that it will accumulate as excessive daydreaming and fantasy. Naturally while listening to the fanciful outpourings of an offspring, you must have one eye fixed on the need of inculcating truthfulness. You must help a child to arrive at the conclusion that a good story is still good without the necessity of pretending that it actually happened.

There are other potentials, but I have given the important ones. Children do not just grow up. The growth of their emotions as well as of their flesh and blood is deeply rooted in the environmental soil of the home. From this soil the emotional plant must draw its sustenance and the direction and nature of its growth are determined early, and frequently cannot be changed. The psychological potentials must be carefully nurtured and tended if maturity is to be the end result.

CHAPTER XIX

ARE YOU A MOM?

As you read the preceding pages, you probably were able to spot quite a few moms and pops among your friends. Some of the case histories undoubtedly reminded you of similar situations in the families right in your own neighborhood. The "pretty addlepate" and the "self-sacrificing mom" are easy to recognize—when it is someone else.

But how about *you?* Are you a mom? Do you have momistic tendencies?

First of all, if this book made you mad, you probably are and have. Second, try to give fair and truthful answers to the forty questions that follow; then turn to the list at the end of the quiz and see how the average mom would answer them.

Answer these questions "yes" or "no" and remember —be frank with yourself:

1. Do you think it wise to give intelligent, honest answers to all the questions your youngsters ask regarding sex?

2. Do you consider children of eight or nine years

of age too young to spend their vacations away from home in summer camp?

3. Do you think even very young children should be allowed the adult privilege of making some decisions for themselves even though in instances their decisions are unwise in your opinion?

4. When you and your husband (or wife) have a serious disagreement do you look to your children for sympathy?

5. Do you think a home should be run in such a manner that the primary consideration is almost *always* that the children's wants and comforts come first?

6. Do you find your sympathies tend in the direction generally of the child who you think is most like yourself?

7. Would you *forbid* your son or daughter to marry someone of whom you do not approve and make them uncomfortable if they were not willing to obey?

8. Do your children take an active part in school and community life?

9. Do you find yourself "running down" or belittling your husband or wife to the children?

10. Do you ever resort to weeping to gain a point with your children?

11. Do you frequently have outbursts of temper when your children misbehave?

12. Do you habitually and secretly discuss your daughter-in-law (or son-in-law) with your married son (or daughter)?

13. Do you ever complain to your married children of the treatment or attitude you receive from their husbands or wives?

14. Do you consider it your duty to help your children form a healthy, normal, and beautiful concept of sex?

15. When you don't feel well, do you complain to your children and look to them for sympathy?

16. If your husband (or wife) punishes a child, do you interfere or argue about it before the child?

17. Do you comfort, pet, and reward a child after it has been justly punished?

18. If you felt you had unjustly punished or scolded a child because you yourself were in a jittery state, would you afterward acknowledge this to the child and talk it out frankly?

19. Do you try to force your children to accept or acknowledge your personal prejudices and ideas of right and wrong as best, even though they may not agree with them?

20. Are you hurt or angry when your children do not accept your judgments and decisions?

21. Are you hurt, openly or secretly, when your children are happy away from home—even though you know they are happy at home also?

22. Do you get your children to obey by giving or promising them presents and rewards?

23. If your children get into difficulties in school, do you usually think it is the fault of the teacher and school?

24. Do you worry when your children are quiet and do not tell you what they are thinking?

25. If your children quarrel with other children, do you generally defend your children and take their side?

26. If your children quarrel between themselves, do you take the part of one consistently?

27. Are you happy and satisfied to see your children going forward as a part of their own times when it means breaking away from the traditional past of your own?

28. Do you consider your children's requests in the matter of clothing and personal appearance and encourage them to make their own selections?

29. When their selections are unwise do you talk over the problem with them adequately?

30. Do you oppose your children's, particularly your son's, participation in rough games like football for fear they might be hurt?

31. Do you accept your share of the responsibility in meting out and carrying through just and necessary punishments of your children?

32. Do you worry about your children's health and spend a great deal of energy and time warding off the *possibility* of colds, sicknesses, or injuries?

33. Do you impress on your children the various family physical weaknesses?

34. When your children make friends of whom you do not approve, do you try to force them to give them up, rather than depending on your child's own ability to come to a proper decision about the friend in question?

35. If you are unhappily married and not well mated sexually, would you (or do you) try to influence your children's selection of marital partners so that their husbands or wives will be as unlike your own as possible?

36. Have you advised or influenced your son or daughter either not to marry or to wait a long time before so doing?

37. Do you believe that an adult son or daughter should devote his life to the care of an aged or chronically ill parent rather than put that parent in a good institution or "home" where they will receive adequate care and comfort?

38. Do you think you should bring your aging father or mother into your home to live if your husband (or wife) objects?

39. If there were an alcoholic in your family, would you consider it reasonable and proper to try to exact promises from your children never to touch alcohol?

40. If the men of your family had all been professors, ministers, professional men, or white-collar workers and your son, who had a real flare for mechanics and a very low scholastic aptitude, wanted to go into a garage business, would you refuse to accept his decision gracefully and belittle his choice?

Here is how the typical mom would answer the questions:

1. No	4. Yes
2. Yes	5. Yes
3. No	6. Yes

7. Yes	24. Yes
8. No	25. Yes
9. Yes	26. Yes
10. Yes	27. No
11. Yes	28. No
12. Yes	29. No
13. Yes	30. Yes
14. No	31. No
15. Yes	32. Yes
16. Yes	33. Yes
17. Yes	34. Yes
18. No	35. Yes
19. Yes	36. Yes
20. Yes	37. Yes
21. Yes	38. Yes
22. Yes	39. Yes
23. Yes	40. Yes

CHAPTER XX

PSYCHIATRY SPEAKS TO DEMOCRACY

Not that they needed it, but perhaps I have provided mothers with some explanation of why they behave as mothers. My main hope, however, is to show moms why they misbehave as moms. I simply cannot believe that any sane woman who has borne children would wish to harm them. If their children's lives were threatened by some immediate danger, like fire or drowning, moms would, and often do, give their own lives to save them. They do not see and understand the more remote threat to something just as precious as life—emotional maturity.

If ever we needed full-blossomed maturity as a national characteristic we need it now. The war is over and won; ahead of us lies the peace. Only if the peace is handled by mature people will it succeed; only if nations as nations reflect maturity can the peace endure.

I define maturity as the ability to stick to a job, the capacity to give more on any job than is asked for, reliability, persistence to carry out a plan regardless of the difficulties, the ability to work with other people under organization and authority, the ability to make decisions, a will to life, flexibility, independence, and tolerance. If all people and all nations had these qualities there could be no wars.

Unfortunately, judging from the record, maturity seems to be largely lacking in the human race—in people, in government, and in nations. A mature world would hardly have embroiled itself in two costly wars in two and one-half decades. A mature world, by being flexible in its ideals and ideas, by working as an organized unit for the good of the whole, by making decisions and per-severing to the goal in mind, by being reliable, and by being tolerant could have avoided war.

We consider ourselves among the most mature of the world's nations. Yet our induction records and Army discharge records show a high percentage of rejections and discharges traceable in a large degree to immaturity and lack of motivation.

Mom is not entirely to blame. She may be the catalyst, but not the main ingredient. Perhaps our general way of life—our "civilization"—should take some of the blame.

In our age, the material achievements of the physical sciences have been truly breath-taking. Rapidly pyra-mided, one upon the other, they now reach a towering height. The peak of the tower is fittingly capped by the atomic bomb. As for speed, almost every day the papers bring word of new and greater speeds attained by air-planes flying from coast to coast or across the oceans.

But how have we used these discoveries? Unfortu-nately, history thus far will have to record that they have been employed as much or more for wanton destruction than for constructive purposes. From the very beginning, the enemy aggressors used them deliberately in a brutal attempt to rule the world. Finally, even we, driven by determination to stop the wholesale slaughter, used them for war.

Material considerations alone, too often impervious to all else but greed, will not suffice to insure the use of these amazing products of physical science for the peace and benefit of mankind. There also must be a freeing of the spiritual essence in all of us and it must be allowed to grow and be applied. All of us must learn, not only in our minds but in our deepest emotions, a decent regard for the dignity of men, all men.

Now, and for a long time past, we have been so materialistically noisy that the faint voice of the spirit has been drowned out. The historians of the future who survey past civilizations will label the current civilization and culture as too externalized—too extroverted. Our mental diseases and nervous breakdowns in most cases are protests against the leveling and regimentation demanded by a strongly extroverted society.

A strongly extroverted civilization is not particularly good, even for the extrovert. It provides too many broad, brilliantly lighted and noisy avenues along which energy may be uselessly expended, too many side shows, too many parades, and too much applause. Altogether there are far too few quiet, shaded retreats in which meditative thought may come to fruitful maturity.

As for the introvert, the quiet individual who wants a little time for reflection, an extroverted society will have little or none of him. Unless he is fortunate enough to find a niche which provides an opportunity for thinking, he is very likely to be pushed around and bruised by encounters with a social stratum which, although on the surface friendly and genial, is underneath hard and unyielding to nonconformists. We are in some danger of producing a tabloid age for tabloid minds.

For a long time mental hygienists have insisted that an appraisal of the values of our civilization is urgently needed. If such an appraisal is fairly done, it will show that our material values must be sharply revised downward. At the present time they exert a power markedly in excess of their actual cultural values. As it stands, there is grave danger that real cultural and spiritual values will be bludgeoned into inarticulate insensibility by materialism. We need quiet places in which to think and something to think about other than machines and bathroom and kitchen gadgets.

The proudest boast of standardized American industry is quantity production. There is reason for pride. Our achievement is little short of genius. Indeed, it is industrial genius. Almost anything from alarm clocks to automobiles can be produced in huge quantities. Each worker at the assembly line contributes his small function, perhaps affixing a nut or bolt or applying a coat of varnish. The few purposeful and synchronized movements made by each worker rub the Aladdin lamp of production and soon there are hundreds and thousands of automobiles or mousetraps or what not. Furthermore, the production machinery may be readily diverted from its original purpose. When airplanes and ships of war and supply were needed, soon they were forthcoming in miraculous numbers.

But there is a price that must be paid for standardized quantity production. Is the accomplishment worth the price? The record of the reduction of hazards and the protection and saving of human lives in American industrial plants is a humanitarian achievement of the first order. It is regrettable that the emotional hazards, the crippling and death of the spirit, are not statistically reckoned.

The thing we have lost in standardized quantity production is a spiritual quality that went into the making of one article, a chair or a table or something else, by one man. Now, excepting as a hobby, almost never does one person make one whole thing.

You will recall the reply given to the traveler by a humble workman in Paris in the Middle Ages. When asked what he was doing he answered proudly, "I am building a cathedral." Inevitably, pride of creation and craftsmanship suffers at the hands of quantity production. The tiny thing that each man does is almost too small and insignificant for his own emotional satisfaction. Unconsciously he feels inferior and belittled. If he has a normal amount of brain power, the repetitive gadget-affixing job is scarcely sufficient to engage more than a fraction of it. He ruminates and broods, becomes anxious, discontented, envious, and sometimes antisocial. Often he is easily victimized into wild-cat strikes. Basically, there is a deep undercurrent of anxiety; and illegal strikes and other ill-advised activities, bountiful with promises, represent frantic efforts to find security. Perhaps in the union the workman finds too much protection. It is a kind of strong and powerful mom which is very solicitous about him and engages to protect him from anyone and anything, provided of course that he remains closely attached to the union. Perhaps the union does too much thinking for the individual workman, at the expense of some of his independence of thought and action.

This is not a criticism of labor unions. They have corrected unfair conditions, ill-treatment and injustices and enormously elevated the material level of the American worker. I doubt if that is sufficient. I doubt, too, that merely higher wages and shorter hours will satisfy the American workman. Unconsciously too much is left unsatisfied, and the unsatisfied area is largely spiritual. No outpouring of material largess will supply the spiritual needs of the worker.

It seems to me that labor unions are in a position to make a superb two-fold contribution. One aspect would be to educate the worker and indoctrinate him not only in his job and his rights, but also in the historical, utilitarian, social, and cultural importance of the finished product to the making of which he contributes, and also to give him a real understanding of his dignity, his obligations and duties in the social structure. Certainly union and employer might profitably bury the hatchet deep enough to cooperate toward the achievement of this objective.

The other facet would involve a certain degree of relinquishment of the worker by the union and the paving of the way for him to attain cultural and spiritual emancipation and growth outside the confines of union structure. In order to move in these directions, it would be necessary for both employers and unions to purge themselves, the employer of some of his prerogatives, the union of certain self-seeking and unscrupulous bosses. Here are objectives which if accomplished would dignify labor, adjust workers culturally and spiritually, and make them strong citadels of national security.

In any event, psychiatrists observe in many of their patients the damage and despiritualizing effect of emotionally uncompensated quantity production labor. These lines from the autobiography of an assembly belt worker may serve as an index of what may happen to the soul of the worker, "It meant going on the assembly, on the line, standing and twisting a dozen bolts on a cylinder head as the moving carriage went past his station, Russ, mind you, threading bolts. This guy with a lion's heart, the fellow who could run anything that moved. And he couldn't do it. He wouldn't. He was clumsy. The rhythm of the belting overhead got into him and slowed him down. The moan and howl and shriek of the machinery made him angry, then mad, then crazy."

There are no tin-punching machines or noisy gears and belts in the occupational therapy departments of mental hospitals. Occupational therapy is nicely individualized and ornamented, seeking gently and tactfully to woo the patient back into the realities of sane and nonpsychoneurotic life, and never at all suggesting mass production.

In my official capacity, I have visited many rehabilitation centers of the Army, Navy, and Air Forces. While there is a serious dearth of trained personnel, the record of occupational therapy is very satisfactory. Service occupational therapy has demonstrated a useful fact which will be applied by civilian occupational therapy. The product may be something practical and dignified, and its making still furnish valuable treatment, bridging the gap between the dangerous helplessness of illness and the activities of everyday life. Mentally and nervously sick returnees, insecure and frightened, are taught how to repair and build their own radios, repair watches, fix their own automobiles, milk cows, make rocking horses and other toys for their children at home, plan and construct in miniature the houses in which they are going to live—and many other things. Many of the men begin to envision the future with less and less apprehension and start to walk toward it with increasingly confident steps. In the Air Forces, it is usual practice, when possible, for the wives of returnee patients to live in the vicinity of the convalescent hospitals. Hand in hand, the husband and wife plan their future. They discuss, argue, modify, and come to satisfactory agreements.

Of these things, the evils of war and the human and democratic catastrophes resulting from the stupid insistence that differences of opinions between nations can be settled only by force of arms; of the need of spiritual barriers against the sordid mass destruction of human life and of the devastation and degradation of the human soul inherent in the products of the exact physical sciences unless they are used constructively; of the need for less haste and less blaring noise and more quiet, planful reflection; of the importance of neutralizing the despiritualizing effect of standardized quantity production and of many other things, Psychiatry speaks with assurance. But there is nothing of which Psychiatry can speak with more confidence and assurance than the danger to our democratic civilizations and cultures from keeping children enwombed psychologically and not permitting them to grow up emotionally and socially. Here is our gravest menace.

Our war experiences—the alarming number of so-called "psychoneurotic" young Americans—point and emphasize this threat to our survival. No one could view this huge test tube of man power, tried and found wanting, without realizing that an extremely important factor was the inability or unwillingness of the American mom and her surrogates to grant the boon of emotional emancipation during childhood. Already we have incurred a large penalty. The threat to our security must not be allowed to go farther.

Finally, again I should like to point out on the social map of democracy the "I and You territory," the land intermediate between individual personal rights, liberties, and privileges and social contributions, duties, and obligations—the area upon which each one of us has a mutual responsibility as well as claim. This area must be a land of fair and mature give-and-take—between people and between nations. It must be a jointly held area of reasonable concessions and decent tolerances. While this area must of necessity have shifting, alterable boundaries, the survival or the death of our democracy depends on a clearer understanding and a more accurate delineation of the "I and You" relationships. Only if the nation is furnished with a maximum supply of true mothers can such clearer understanding, more accurate delineation and, indeed, safeguarding of the personal and social essence of democracy be accomplished.

Mom is a surface fissure warning us of deeper defects.

CHAPTER XXI

OUT OF SWADDLING CLOTHES

Almost five years have elapsed since the initial publication of *Their Mothers' Sons*. As this revision is issued, it would seem appropriate to review briefly the situation.

From an unexpected quarter, Russia, comes support for the main theme of this book, that childhood experiences affect markedly not only the behavior of individual adults, but the psychological personality markings of nations.* It would be at once an over-simplification and an exaggeration to state that the practice of swaddling babies (which excepting the elite and intelligentsia castes is universally followed by the great number of Russians) produces their national psychology. On the other hand, it would be a serious omission not to say that swaddling does influence profoundly the psychology of the Russian masses—a psychology that must be understood and reckoned with in any intelligent estimate of the East-West crisis.

Babies are swaddled, i.e., tightly bandaged (legs straight, arms to sides) for about the first nine months of their lives. Observers liken swaddled babies to "sticks" or "sausages." Exploration of the environment by the infant

---

* *The People of Great Russia*, by Geoffrey Gorer and John Rickman, M.D., Chanticleer Press, Inc., New York, 1950.

is rendered impossible. Furthermore, the infant's vocal protests are reduced by popping into its mouth when it cries a comforter or *nib*. Usually the *nib* is a rag containing chewed food and it acts as an effective plug. From time to time, for nursing, and for infrequent bathing, the baby is unswaddled, but then immediately re-bandaged. The baby is apt to be under the care of a very superstitious old woman, the *babushka* or grandmother, who, however, often is not the blood grandmother, or even related to the child.

It seems altogether likely that in considerable degree this childhood situation tends to favor the inculcation of personal and mass hostility and guilt reactions. From the abrupt alternations between being tightly bound and temporarily freed, one would expect extreme swings of attitudes and behavior, for instance, from violence to gentleness.

During the Russian Civil War, a company of Red soldiers "came to a burnt-out village without a living soul, and suddenly they heard a baby crying; they looked and found a baby just a few weeks old, alive, lying beside the corpse of his mother. Well, half drunk and dirty bandits though they were, they took the baby and then they asked, 'Who will nurse the baby?'. So they invaded the next village and took a woman with a baby of the same age and killed her husband and said to her, 'Citizen, you must serve the Revolution!'. They dragged this woman round with them several weeks, and made her nurse her own baby and the baby of the company. They took a pair of scales and used to weigh both babies on the balance every day to make certain she was feeding the company baby properly. If the company baby weighed less than hers did, they used to beat her for cheating; but during the fighting, they would all protect this woman and her two babies and keep them in the rear. When they finally returned to Moscow, they gave the woman one of the highest awards and made her chief nurse in an institution for orphans. This is just one example of the mixture of brutality and cruelty and sympathy and warmth. In the midst of battle they were more engaged in protecting the babies than their own selves." *

There is only the space to indicate very briefly the traits of Russian character which directly or indirectly may be derived from infant swaddling. Physical sufferings are endured stoically and there is indifference to the sufferings of others. There is an unconscious, rather diffused hostility toward those who are "different." The tendency to see potential enemies encompassing them on all sides is shared by the elite, but they would like to see the hostility of the masses toward others more purposeful and longer sustained—a deep, unrelenting and permanent hatred. Herein is a source of war danger. Should the leaders feel there was a likelihood that the hostility of the masses might be turned against them, they might precipitate a war to divert the hatred from themselves. The masses resign themselves to firm authority. Perhaps one of the

* From *The People of Great Russia*, by Gorer and Rickman, Chanticleer Press, Inc., New York, 1950.

gravest risks of war would be involved in a policy of vacillation between strength and weakness, consistency and inconsistency, on the part of the Western Powers. Finally, all important is the idealization and idolization of the Leader, the merging of the masses into him. He is the ever present, always watchful, the rewarding, the punishing, universal mom.

I am not naive enough to assert that there is a close analogy between the swaddling of Russian babies and its psychological effects and maternal and parental emotional possessiveness of children, too prevalent in our country. Of course, there are suggestive similarities. The personalities of many of our children are firmly "bandaged" by selfish and possessive maternal and paternal "love." Unrelenting, non-explanatory parental authority has much the same binding effect. In the school and in play with other children, the "swaddling" is loosened. Back in the home, they are psychologically reswaddled either by "love" or rigid discipline. At least in one area it is fair to infer a similarity of effect between the practice of Russian swaddling and our own dangerously increasing tendency to possess our children emotionally. Both systems dangerously inhibit normal psychological growth, halting children at levels of emotional immaturity. They are not prepared to meet life in its personal, social and national responsibilities on even a minimal basis of the give and take and necessary self-decision of adult living. Such children are condemned to dissipate their future lives in a never ending search for mom surrogates, people and "movements" with whom and with which and into which they may merge and identify so that they need not think for themselves nor feel guilty for their behavior.

The tragedy of the situation is that Psychiatry and its allied disciplines do have enough information to write an approximately correct formula for the production of the beginnings of emotional maturity in children. I repeat, it is a satisfactory distribution and balance of the ingredients of being wanted, loved, nurtured, protected and being made to feel secure and at the same time being given the opportunity and the help to grow up emotionally. If this formula could be applied on a wide scale, many more very much needed emotionally grown-up, self-decisive and self-acting citizens would be produced.

There is an erroneous idea that there is no place for guidance and discipline during childhood. It harks back to the days when it was believed that children should be permitted complete and unadulterated self-expression, without even the slightest adult protest or interference. This was the time when I heard the fourteen-year-old son of a physician friend of mine say to his mother, who had asked him to get something at the corner grocery store, "Mother, I do not choose to do it." Fortunately, the fallacies of ultra self-expression for children are now clearly recognized. No less an authority than Anna Freud testifies that youngsters left without any guidance or discipline flounder helplessly and become confused and insecure. I believe that the original thought of promoting self-expression was that it would prevent the development of anxiety. A little experience with anxiety during childhood, perhaps the amount derived from some insistence upon a reasonable degree of conformity to the personal and social rights of others, would seem to be a necessary prelude and preparation for being able to meet the inevitable and numerous anxiety-producing situations of adult life.

There is a soft under-belly of immaturity in our democratic culture. It is related to the deficits of opportunities to acquire during childhood a reasonable degree of emotional growth. I hesitate to use the criterion of war as a measuring rod of emotional maturity. War is archaic and bestial and, in some sense, measures a man by his willingness and capacity to kill other men. Nevertheless, war cannot be disregarded since, for a long time to come, we seem doomed to live in an atmosphere of war and rumors of war. Furthermore, many of the psychiatric breakdowns of World War II were not per se a matter of war. They merely occurred in the setting of war, rather than being occasioned by it. These were the breakdowns motivated by emotional infantilism and would have been and, indeed, often had been, apparent in civilian life. In the enormously large number of young men who evaded the draft; in a very sizeable segment of those who had to be discharged for psychoneuroses, even though never exposed to the hardships and hazards of the battle area; in the alarming proportion of battle psychiatric casualties; in the necessity of lowering psychological induction standards which faces us, and in many other considerations there is a wide segment of emotional immaturity.

From war we should learn first how to dispense with war and then we must learn, and at once, a sounder evaluation of our democratic civilization and put it into practice as soon as possible or else it will be too late. A considerable number of the young men discharged from the Army after a short trial of service and the larger number rejected at induction are best described as having been temperamentally unsuited for military service. True, they did have various indefinite neurotic and psychosomatic symptoms and some of them showed psychopathic traits (frequently absent without leave, intolerant of discipline, constantly grousing, stirring up discontent in others, always at sick call, etc.) but as every service psychiatrist knew, the basic reason why they could not be accepted or had to be discharged was because they could not adjust to military life. The record shows, too, that the majority had not adjusted satisfactorily in civilian life.

One makes no progress at all by precipitating arguments as to whether these men were really sick. Of course they were sick, even if sometimes there was a considerable element of pretense. Much more important is it to know what the sickness expressed. What was its origin? What is its significance for our democracy?

The psychiatric reading at the first level beneath the surface symptoms apparently discovered in these men sometimes unconsciously, but often consciously, not only an inability but also an unwillingness to serve. Here was a profound disturbance of the "I" and "You" relationship. The origin was in childhood. As children these young men had learned only to take, not to give.

There is no need of indicting those who insist only on the rights and privileges accorded by a democracy and neither understand the duties nor the obligations incurred. Only in very small degree are they responsible for their undemocratic behavior and the dangerous situation that has been produced. Faulty human biology and constitution cannot be blamed too much. For one thing, in the group under consideration as revealed in the huge laboratory of manpower where adequate soldier material was sought, generally speaking there was not so much evidence of intellectual inferiority but rather was there obvious evidence of personal and social immaturity. Much more indictable were defects in childhood training, particularly in child-parent relationships—grievous failures in teaching concessions in the matter of so-called personal rights. Apparently a reasonable amount of social obligation and responsiveness was not learned. In the growing personality, the "I" became enormously large, the "You" pitifully small. Too often there was not even a minimum of habituation by practice of contribution to the social welfare of the community and nation. Since such lessons can be impressed but very faintly by verbal precept and deeply only by example, one cannot escape the conclusion that far too many adults responsible for the emotional development and spiritual growth of children are themselves emotionally immature. Consequently in their attitudes and behavior, they are basically undemocratic.

There are many other soft spots in our democracy, festerings from the core of emotional immaturity. For instance, there is the veteran problem in its many and varied ramifications. *Obviously, there can be no compensation, monetary or in other ways, which can requite the debt of patriotic service well rendered.* But as everyone knows, some veterans, spurred on by selfish propaganda, are misled into more and more demands, even though they may be quite unreasonable. I venture to say that much emotional immaturity would be found in this group of veterans more eager to receive than to give.

In the many demands made upon and supplications to the government by various groups, the amount of "take" attitude is huge, the quantity of "give" is microscopic. True enough, many of the contentions of labor, of management, of agriculture, of old age and other pension groups, of isolationism and anti-isolationism, and of a thousand and one "movements" seeking political and financial support, strictly speaking, are right and just enough. But they are too single-tracked. The heavy emphasis is on rights and privileges. There is a flagrant disregard of obligations and duties. Only their own isolated areas are in the focus of their thoughts and actions. The picture is not seen as a whole. Obviously the government, which is the people, cannot give everything to everyone. Cooperation, concession, compromise are hallmarks of genuine maturity. One begins to suspect that at the roots of the seemingly irreconcilable conflicts between various groups, there is less of economic pressure than is commonly believed and more of the result of the fact that too many of us in our childhoods became habituated to too much taking for ourselves, too little of giving to others.

A French workman, reflecting sadly upon the conditions which made it possible for the Nazi to trample France under heel, among other things said: "We have lacked an ideal. We came to imagine that the proper duty of man was to arrange an easy way of life, individualistic to the point of selfishness. We saw no other purpose than the ability to satisfy our wants. We looked upon the state as the universal purveyor and we always spoke of our due, seldom of our duties. We persisted in our errors. For one thing, we persisted in leveling the nation down and in imagining that the state would prove an everlasting milch cow. . . . Tell all this to the Americans and warn them at the same time of the perils that may befall democracy everywhere when it forgets that free men have duties as well as rights."

The mere fact that, all in all, democracy represents the highest level in social progress achieved thus far is not sufficient. There must be a strong, unified front of the people, all the people, a solid front produced by thoughtful compromises, concessions and sacrifices. It is a fallacy to believe that a democracy cannot be overcome. Sparta vanquished Athens and the clock of democratic civilization and culture was turned back for centuries.

When there are large segments of emotional immaturity in a people and their leaders, too, are immature, then there emerges a very serious situation. Intellectual stature is far less involved than is commonly appreciated. Superior intellect, even genius, may co-exist with emotional infantilism. When, for instance, at the UN conference table, the Russian delegates passionately arraign us and beat their breasts at the ogre of capitalistic imperialism, of course they do not believe more than one-tenth of their own harangues. (A new word bids fair to be included in our language—to malik. To malik is to tell a lie, which the utterer of the falsehood not only knows is a lie, but knows, too, that those who hear it know it is a lie.) They are too intelligent for that. True, the policy is dictated by the masters in the Kremlin. However, the manner of carrying out that policy and its details are not ordered from Moscow. The words that are used, the gestures, the mode of "taking the walk" when their will is opposed, the childish way in which the veto is given, all these are the equivalent of a child's "If you won't play like I say, I won't play with you at all." Such behavior is streaked with immaturity. It is the most dangerous kind of immaturity, dangerous for Russia, dangerous for us, dangerous for all the world. Conceivably, very powerful economic, political and military weapons might be placed in the hands of those who are not mature enough to realize that they should be handled with extreme care.

At least in our country we are blessed with some mature and thoughtful leaders. Nevertheless, in our own legislative halls and in highly placed governmental seats, there are men who have not outgrown their emotional diapers which, barring the kind of miracle that rarely happens, are destined to become their shrouds. We are becoming increasingly thoughtful of the physical health of candidates for high office. It is a sign of progress. It would be even better if we scanned the records of prospective candidates not only as to their bodies and I.Q.'s, but very searchingly as to the pattern of their emotional behavior. In the face of crises which now abound, it is extremely important for us to know whether they can be counted upon to conduct the affairs of state in thoughtful, grown-up fashion.

No matter upon which cross-section of human behavior the psychiatrist turns his gaze, inevitably and very soon he focuses upon childhood. Childhood is the tide time for making sound, flexible personalities for adult life. Conversely, if in childhood the pattern laid down is decidedly immature, then only major upheavals will change the course of events in the life march of time and major upheavels are rare.

Is anyone naive enough to believe that violent prejudice and intolerance can appear spontaneously in adult life? Of course, they are germinated in childhood. In the early life of some children, far too many, there are dark and noisome places; pestilential areas of ignorance and intolerance. These unfortunate children are inoculated with the virus of hate, hate for anything "foreign," even though the "foreigners" may live only a few blocks away. In the daily family life, there is inculcated into plastic personalities opposition, suspicion and violent reactions toward people who are "different"—different in color, race or creed—different in anything, even though it be only in the food they eat or the clothes they wear. From the ranks of these children become adults, poisoned in their thinking, attitudes and behavior, there are recruited the followers and sometimes the leaders of the multi-colored shirted and hooded organizations. Occasionally a dangerous, large-scale dictator is produced. The smallest amount of propaganda suffices to recruit such people for homicidal mobs. Incendiary speeches, waving a few flags, beating the drums suffice to unleash their hate and make them eager to fight aggressive, unnecessary and unjust wars.

From such thinking and behavior it is not too long a step to the operation of dictatorships. Blessedly, in a real democracy, there is this saving grace: The lips of the defenders of honest minority groups are not sealed. Whenever there is unjust discrimination, there is no lack of strong and articulate defenders from outside the group that is being unfairly treated. In a democracy that is to survive, the national superego or conscience must become increasingly stronger, more vigilant, and more expressive. I have enough faith in the destiny of our nation to believe that in spite of many false steps, much stumbling and falling, we are striving to approach and kneel at the altar of the true ideals of democracy. I take it that such striving must include unremitting effort to soften the impacts and lessen the penalties to be paid by the victims of natural inequalities, coupled with constant, earnest, vigorous and forceful action in leveling artificial inequalities and barriers. Our striving and the reaching of our goal will be greatly retarded if too many of our citizens are emotionally immature. They can neither understand the obligations of a virile democracy nor can they assist in attaining its objective and ideals.

Dictatorships flourish in the soil of emotional immaturity of the people. At this time, by majority, if not unanimous, opinion, the id, that is the power drive and in a sense, the baser part of the composite personality of the rulers of Russia is unleashed and rampant and the superego, or conscience, is at the nadir. This is not per se by reason of the enslavement of millions of their own people, their mass murders and the rape of small nations. Such crimes may be found in the histories of all powerful nations. The real crime of the Soviet and other dictators is that in this day their behavior is a throw-back—an atavism. It is as if modern Psychiatry would destroy its scientific and humane equipment, suddenly take a backward step through two centuries and again chain, beat and torture the helpless mentally sick.

Perhaps it is a coincidence, but if so, it is a highly suspicious one, that there is a similarity of pattern in the child lives of three modern dictators—Hitler, Mussolini and Stalin.* At the hands of their fathers they all suffered non-loving, brutal authority and probably became too deeply attached to their mothers. It is well to remember

---

* The author has access to the account of a reliable eye-witness of Stalin's childhood in his native village in Georgia, Russia.

that fear engendered and dammed back in childhood is likely to produce hostility and aggressiveness directed against the environment in adult life. This is a commonplace observance by psychiatrists in the life histories of psychotic and neurotic patients. It is likely that the cold, rigid father authority of their childhoods conditioned in the dictators a hatred of all authority other than their own. Could it not be that in their ruthless behavior toward the helpless, the leading motif is revenge for the indignities and pain inflicted upon them as children? It is dangerous to entrust power to those adults who have not had reasonably emotionally healthy childhoods. The pathological compromises made in their twisted minds may mean misery and catastrophe for millions of human beings.

Suppose by some bold step forward in human social progress our own and other nations did achieve a large amount and high degree of emotional maturity. What then? Of course, there would still be many "thens" but they would not be too great and forbidding. Economic, political, ideological and spiritual difficulties could not escape solution in a grown-up, mature world founded in and bound together in the love and cooperation of a brotherhood of man.

At present this is little more than a pious hope. Facing the situation realistically, what is to be the outcome? We know what we have to fear. What may we hope for? When confronted with grave personal danger, men may and frequently do look the danger straight in the face and scorn it. Man *can* rise above self. It is as if his super-ego, the nobler part of man, usually pitifully weak and futile, suddenly gains great strength, takes charge of the personality, silencing the baser demands of the id, commanding the services of the ego, pulling the man up by his bootstraps, setting him down upon a high level of sacrifice.

In the great disasters of the sea, like the *Titanic,* men handed women and children into the life boats and returned to the deck, sinking into the ocean to the strains of the ship's band. In the annals of the American Red Cross, a long record of disasters by storm, flood, fire and blast, there are shining accounts of gallantry, men giving their lives that others could live.

Heroic episodes of human behavior were common in World War II. It is hard to believe we can hate our neighbors and remember the immortal scene of the four chaplains of different faiths, hand in hand, sinking into the sea so that there would be four more life belts for others.

Never was the need so great! Never can it be greater! May we be given the strength, the faith and the courage to bridge the huge gap between our baser selves and our feeble aspirations to bind together all people in the fraternity of common understanding, tolerance and love.

There is one other powerful weapon. It is education. Give Psychiatry and the other humanitarian disciplines the wherewithal to find out more about human beings, to implement what it knows and what it will learn in the future. The Government spent two billion dollars to make the atom bomb. Comparatively only a few paltry dollars can be found to write and spread the gospel of Mental Hygiene. If we really wish to strike a blow for democracy, let us give our children the fifth and greatest of freedoms—the right to grow up emotionally. Education takes time. Time is running out. May we be granted the grace of enough time. For every one, you and me, each one of us, whoever and wherever we are, the appointed time is at hand.